CURRENT TOPICS IN

DEVELOPMENTAL BIOLOGY

VOLUME 10

CURRENT TOPICS IN
DEVELOPMENTAL BIOLOGY

EDITED BY

A. A. MOSCONA

DEPARTMENTS OF BIOLOGY AND PATHOLOGY
THE UNIVERSITY OF CHICAGO
CHICAGO, ILLINOIS

ALBERTO MONROY

C.N.R. LABORATORY OF MOLECULAR EMBRYOLOGY
ARCO FELICE (NAPLES), ITALY

VOLUME 10
Experimental Systems for Analysis
of Multicellular Organization

1975

ACADEMIC PRESS   New York • San Francisco • London

A Subsidiary of Harcourt Brace Jovanovich, Publishers

ACADEMIC PRESS, INC.
111 Fifth Avenue, New York, New York 10003

United Kingdom Edition published by
ACADEMIC PRESS, INC. (LONDON) LTD.
24/28 Oval Road, London NW1

LIBRARY OF CONGRESS CATALOG CARD NUMBER: 66-28604

ISBN 0–12–153110–4

PRINTED IN THE UNITED STATES OF AMERICA

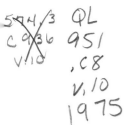
CONTENTS

CHAPTER 4. **Phenomena of Cellular Recognition in Sponges**

G. VAN DE VYVER

CHAPTER 5. **Freshwater Sponges as a Material for the Study of Cell Differentiation**

R. RASMONT

CHAPTER 6. **Differentiation of the Golgi Apparatus in the Genetic Control of Development**

W. G. WHALEY, MARIANNE DAUWALDER, AND T. P. LEFFINGWELL

LIST OF CONTRIBUTORS

Numbers in parentheses indicate the pages on which the authors' contributions begin.

BACCIO BACCETTI, *Institute of Zoology, University of Siena, Siena, Italy* (103)

MARIANNE DAUWALDER, *The Cell Research Institute, The University of Texas at Austin, Austin, Texas* (161)

T. P. LEFFINGWELL, *The Cell Research Institute, The University of Texas at Austin, Austin, Texas* (161)

FRANCIS J. MANASEK, *Departments of Cardiology and Pathology, The Children's Hospital Medical Center and Department of Anatomy, Harvard Medical School, Boston, Massachusetts; and Department of Anatomy, The University of Chicago, Chicago, Illinois* (35)

JANE OVERTON, *Department of Biology, Whitman Laboratory, University of Chicago, Chicago, Illinois* (1)

R. RASMONT, *Laboratoire de Biologie Animale et Cellulaire, Université Libre de Bruxelles, Brussels, Belgium* (141)

G. VAN DE VYVER, *Laboratoire de Biologie Animale et Cellulaire, Université Libre de Bruxelles, Brussels, Belgium* (123)

W. G. WHALEY, *The Cell Research Institute, The University of Texas at Austin, Austin, Texas* (161)

vii

PREFACE

It has been pointed out to the Editors that the publication of the tenth volume in this series represents an important and happy occasion worthy of special notice. While we deeply appreciate this expression of encouragement, and are gratified by the acceptance and usefulness of this publication, we also wonder if the metric system has not unduly conditioned all of us to assign a special importance to decimal repeats. We have looked upon each one of the previous volumes as a significant and special contribution to the literature in Developmental Biology. Frankly, keeping up with the rapid progress in this field has been more to our liking than celebrating past accomplishments. Perhaps significantly, the ninth and tenth volumes appear almost simultaneously, endeavoring to catch up with some of the exciting and important current research in the field of development and differentiation.

We wish to thank the contributors to Volumes 9 and 10 for meeting the aims, standards, and deadlines of *Current Topics in Developmental Biology*. We also thank the staff of Academic Press for their efforts and cooperation.

A. A. Moscona
Alberto Monroy

CONTENTS OF PREVIOUS VOLUMES

CHAPTER 1

EXPERIMENTS WITH JUNCTIONS OF THE ADHAERENS TYPE[1]

Jane Overton

DEPARTMENT OF BIOLOGY
WHITMAN LABORATORY
UNIVERSITY OF CHICAGO
CHICAGO, ILLINOIS

I. Introduction

There are a number of specialized surface structures by which cells adhere that in many cases can be clearly distinguished by electron microscopy. New distinctions between junctional types continue to be made (for reviews, see McNutt and Weinstein, 1973; Overton, 1974). Adhesion is considered the primary function of some, such as the desmosome (Farquhar and Palade, 1963), but it is also a property of junctions, such as the nexus, which are generally considered to have other major functions (DeHaan and Sachs, 1972; Loewenstein, 1973). In addition, cells adhere by surfaces where no natural morphologically distinguishable junctions are present. Recently, techniques have become available for marking specific surface sites on such areas of the cell membrane (e.g., Karnovsky and Unanue, 1973; Singer and Nicolson, 1972; Smith and Revel, 1973; Raff and De Petris, 1973). Thus a considerable number of cell surface markers are available for use in experimental studies of cell

[1] Aided by grants from the Public Health Service, CA-14599, and the National Science Foundation, GB-38669

adhesion, which have a variety of advantages. This review will consider primarily work which has been done with the desmosome (macula adhaerens) using the term in the sense of Farquhar and Palade (1963). This junction was one of the few to be clearly described at the time the work reported here was initiated (Overton, 1962), and it has continued to prove useful as a marker.

The desmosome or macula adhaerens exists in its mature form typically as a symmetrical structure spanning two cells and therefore requires coordinated activity in adjacent cells for its formation. In vertebrate tissues oval or rounded plaques, generally about 0.2–0.3 μm in diameter and 140 Å in thickness, lie in adjacent cells about 40 Å below the cell membrane and are found in perfect phase with each other. At this region the two plasma membranes are usually straight or only slightly curved and lie parallel, separated by a space of 250 Å or more in width. This intercellular region is moderately electron dense in thin sections and contains a more dense central stratum running parallel to the membranes. The central stratum is also apparent in freeze-etched preparations as a condensation of material (Staehelin et al., 1969). Staining with ruthenium red (Kelly, 1966) as well as with lanthanum (Rayns et al., 1969) suggests that fibrils or strands in the intercellular space connect the central stratum with the adjacent cell membranes. The desmosome plaques in the cytoplasm are typically very electron dense. Plaques are associated with tonofilaments of 100 Å in diameter, which may be more or less extensive. Stereomicrographs have indicated that many if not all such filaments form loops running toward the plaques and back into the cytoplasm (Kelly, 1966). Freeze-cleave studies show closely packed granules or short segments of fine filaments on membrane faces (Breathnach et al., 1972a,b; McNutt and Weinstein, 1973), and indicate that the desmosome sites on both faces of the cleaved membranes have similar arrangements of filament segments (McNutt and Weinstein, 1973). Thus the structure of the membrane as well as that of the intercellular and cortical cytoplasmic regions is distinctive. This brief account of the major features of desmosome structure gives some indication of its potential usefulness as a marker. Differences in the extent or prominence of these various components exist between species, and between different tissues of the same animal which together with its symmetry make the desmosome a potentially useful tool for studies of cell interaction.

In addition to the relatively precise and symmetrical structure of the desmosome itself, this adhesive junction as well as junctions of the intermediate type termed zonulae or fasciae adhaerentes (Farquhar and Palade, 1963; Fawcett and McNutt, 1969) have the advantage that the cytoplasm of the cell may be more or less extensively organized in close relation to these sites in an obvious way. Tonofilaments may extend from the macula adhaerens deep into the cytoplasm; 50 Å filaments which form arrowhead complexes with heavy meromyosin (Ishikawa *et al.*, 1969) are associated with the zonula adhaerens; and, in the most extreme example, the fascia adhaerens of muscle is the point of insertion of myofibrils. Likewise, in arthropods, the cytoplasm may be permeated by microtubules oriented in relation to junctions of the adhaerens type. In addition to these well known associations, many cases have been described in which mitochondria are associated with maculae adhaerentes in both embryonic and adult veterbrate tissue, and in invertebrates (see Overton, 1974, for review). The association appears to be a close one, since the mitochondrial membrane may be flattened in the area of contact (Joyon *et al.*, 1964; Noirot-Timothée and Noirot, 1967), or in broken cells an empty plasma membrane may be left except for a mitochondrion retained at the desmosome site (Tandler and Hoppel, 1970). Other cytoplasmic components that have been associated with adhering junctions are peroxisomes (Tandler and Hoppel, 1970), and ciliary rootlets in ascidians (Levi and Porte, 1964) and rotifers (Clément and Fouillet, 1970). These examples indicate that the location of adhaerens junctions may be more or less closely related to the spatial organization of the cytoplasm. When desmosomes develop, surface densities form first and tonofilaments become associated with them only later (see Section III). Therefore, if one could control the location of the surface plaque, one might partially influence the internal organization of the cell. Thus it is at least conceivable that study of these junctions might be an approach to the study of cell polarity.

Groups of junctions on the cell surface are present in characteristic complexes and may be intimately related (e.g., Farquhar and Palade, 1963; Friend and Gilula, 1972). There are a few particularly striking examples of positioning of junctions in relation to the polarity of the tissue. Kelly (1966) reports that the hemidesmosomes on the basal surface of epithelial cells in the tail fin of the newt *Taricha torosa* are elongate with the long axes oriented parallel to the anteroposterior axis of the tail. Also, in the epidermis around the electroreceptor in a mormyrid fish (Szabo and Wersäll, 1970) desmosomes joining narrow regions of cell processes are arranged back to back in perfect register, so that at low magnification this results in the appearance of numerous parallel striated bands running at right angles to the free surface. A similar juxtaposition of desmosomes occurs in the Schwann cell (Hama, 1959), and a tendency toward this arrangement can be seen in groups of two to three desmosomes in other tissues (e.g., McNutt and Weinstein, 1973; Fig. 4). In other cases desmosomes may lie in a tandem arrangement (e.g., Overton,

1962). Examples of this type suggest that a suitable system for experimental analysis may be found in which the arrangement of junctions can be used as a marker of tissue polarity. As pointed out by Whitten (1973) insect tissue may be particularly favorable material for study of precisely aligned cell components. The relation between junction formation and tissue structure has to date been considered largely only in connection with descriptive accounts of normal development.

Finally, situations in which abnormal growth occurs might be exploited. We know that many cell surface changes occur under these conditions, but we have as yet no clear concepts as to the relation between these changes and alterations in growth (Pardee, 1971). Desmosomes may be deficient in some epithelia undergoing malignant transformation (McNutt and Weinstein, 1969) or in certain tumors they may be present with greater frequency than normal (Hruban et al., 1972). In other tumors they may show abnormal morphology. Single plaques may occur on lateral cell surfaces with no corresponding partner in the adjacent cell, or plaques may be unusually large or thick (Hruban et al., 1972). It is possible that material of this sort will be found useful in studies in which cells of different types are confronted.

These are speculative suggestions as to the use of desmosomes in the examination of cell interactions. Very little work of this kind has been done as yet. In this review some recent findings concerning the structure of adhaerens junctions will be described, followed by consideration of what is known of their development, their fate upon cell isolation, and after recombination of cells of like and of unlike types. As work of this kind progresses it should become possible to answer certain questions regarding conditions controlling formation of these adhesive structures.

II. The Structure of Adhaerens Junctions

Although progress has been made in defining cell surface junctions morphologically, we have as yet little information concerning their chemical composition. Isolation of gap junctions has been achieved in purified form, and a beginning has been made with chemical analysis (Goodenough and Stoeckenius, 1972), but virtually nothing is known about the desmosome. Desmosome-rich fractions have been prepared (Borysenko and Revel, 1973), but no chemical analyses are yet available. This situation puts distinct limitations on the type of experimental approaches that can be made at the present time. Some clues concerning composition and structure have been found, however, through cytochemical staining and enzymic digestion. These approaches have suggested that the structures defined as maculae adhaerentes in vertebrate tissues by Farquhar and Palade (1963) may in fact be of more than one type.

Enzymic treatment of tissue sections has shown that the desmosome plaques are readily and selectively digested with pepsin, while the tonofilaments remain intact (Douglas *et al.*, 1970; Jessen, 1970). Wolff and Schreiner (1971) observed that the plaques were removed by trypsin while Douglas *et al.* (1970) working with different material found them trypsin resistant. The intercellular component of the desmosome is stained by ruthenium red (Kelly, 1966) and the periodic acid silver methenamine reaction (Rambourg and Leblond, 1967) suggesting that this region contains mucopolysaccharide. Benedetti and Emmelot (1967) stained neuranimidase-sensitive sialic acid in isolated membrane preparations with colloidal iron hydroxide and observed that staining granules were present in the intercellular regions of desmosomes after they had been loosened by treatment with EDTA. Thus the intercellular region of the desmosome appears to contain some components common to the rest of the cell coat. As noted above, this intercellular region if stained with ruthenium red (Kelly, 1966) or treated with lanthanum (Rayns *et al.*, 1969) shows evidence of fibrillar elements. The work of Rayns *et al.* (1969) is particularly suggestive of a regular structure in this region consisting of side arms extending from the central stratum to the two cell surfaces.

In a more recent study, Borysenko and Revel (1973) have treated a number of different tissues with proteolytic enzymes and chelating agents in order to compare the effects on desmosome disruption. In all the stratified squamous epithelia tested, namely, frog skin, human oral mucosa, and cat and rat esophagus, desmosomes were disrupted by trypsin but showed no apparent effect after EDTA treatment, whereas the reverse was true in simple columnar epithelia. Frog tongue, esophagus, and cardiac glands as well as rat ileum and colon were unaffected by trypsin, whereas EDTA promoted separation of cells at the region of the desmosome. Fine structure studies of junctions in these tissues after treatment with a number of agents have suggested two possible models for the organization of the extracellular space. When the junction is sensitive to trypsin, the central stratum may contain a trypsin-digestible protein while the side arms may be composed of protein or glycoprotein not susceptible to trypsin digestion. On the other hand, in EDTA-sensitive junctions the side arms may be held in register by calcium bridges between anionic groups in opposed side arms. The central stratum could be lacking here, and instead a central density could be produced by superposition of the ends of the side arms. Thus distinct differences in reagent sensitivities of desmosomes in different tissues suggest fundamental biochemical differences in the intercellular regions of these junctions.

Differences in sensitivity to reagents may not only exist between desmosomes of different tissues but also between desmosomes of the same tissue at different developmental stages (Rosenblith and Revel, 1972). Larval amphibian epidermis shows a well defined sequence of sensitivities, young larvae have EDTA-sensitive and trypsin-resistant desmosomes, while at metamorphosis they become trypsin sensitive and EDTA resistant. Embryonic rat tissues also have different sensitivities from the same adult tissues. These findings are important in the present connection, since if cells of two tissues that form maculae adhaerentes of different types are opposed, one might reasonably expect a different response than between two cells that form the same type of junction.

Hemidesmosomes (Kelly, 1966), so named because they resemble one half of a desmosome, lie on the basal surface of epithelia and form adhesive sites with the substratum. They are similar to desmosomes since they consist of a localized density at the cell surface with which tonofilaments are associated and have been shown to include a local modification of membrane structure (Kelly and Shienvold, 1973). However, differences in morphology between these structures and desmosomes within the same cells have been reported. In the desmosome both membrane faces bear 80–100 Å granules or filaments (McNutt and Weinstein, 1973), whereas in the hemidesmosome the A face bears particles of 200–300 Å and the B face has corresponding indentations (Kelly and Shienvold, 1973). In amphibian epidermis, fibers approaching the plaque of a hemidesmosome form a much more tightly packed bundle and the plaque is ellipsoidal while that of desmosomes in these cells is nearly round (Kelly, 1966). In human epidermis the hemidesmosome does not contain a clearly defined plaque (Brody, 1968), and in the chick corneal epithelium the hemidesmosomes also have no prominent plaques next to the plasma membrane and are distinctly wedge-shaped as seen in cross section (Hay and Revel, 1969). It has been possible to take advantage of some of these differences in the chick corneal epithelium to distinguish the two different sorts of surface associated densities under experimental conditions.

There has been less study of zonulae and fasciae adhaerentes (Farquhar and Palade, 1963). These junctions typically do not have cytoplasmic condensations in the form of distinct plaques associated with them, but show a wider and more diffuse cytoplasmic density just below the cell membrane in the region of the junction. The intercellular space is typically narrower (150–250 Å) than that of the macula adhaerens and the intercellular material is usually amorphous. Zonulae and fasciae adhaerentes are generally considered to differ only in size and extent, the zonulae forming a band around the cell and the fasciae being present in patches. However, it is possible that these junctions are more diverse. For example, the fascia adhaerens of the pigeon heart muscle is exceptional since it shows a pronounced dense lamina dividing the intercellular region and running parallel to the cell membranes (McNutt, 1970).

Zonulae and fasciae adhaerentes seem to be scarcely related to maculae adhaerentes other than in having an adhesive function. In addition to the differences noted above, the structure of the cell membrane in the junctional region is different. This has been best studied in the fascia adhaerens of muscle (McNutt and Weinstein, 1973), where the outer face of the junctional membrane is smoother since it bears relatively few particles compared to the outer face of the nonjunctional plasma membrane. Thus both fascia- and macula-associated membrane differ in conformation from the nonjunctional cell membrane and also from each other. Another major difference stressed by McNutt and Weinstein (1973) is that the intracellular fibrils attached to the desmosomes are 100 Å in diameter and do not form arrowheads with heavy meromyosin, whereas those associated with zonulae and fasciae are 50 Å in diameter and will do so (Ishikawa et al., 1969).

When cells are dispersed and allowed to reaggregate, characteristic tissue patterns reform (Moscona, 1960; Steinberg, 1962). In such cell associations, as in vivo, all types of intercellular junctions may develop. In fact only a few situations are known in which cells form junctions of a single type. Revel et al. (1971) have examined both BHK21 cells and brown fat cells of young mice by freeze-cleaving so that large areas of the membrane could be viewed; only small gap junctions were observed, but this is a highly exceptional situation. If one is considering large areas of the cell surface in thin sections, the desmosome is perhaps the most readily distinguished junction since the plaques are typically heavily staining, and they are precisely paired. The zonula adhaerens is also easily recognized in its characteristic position just below the free surface of the cell. In addition, in certain tissue, such as muscle, the fasciae adhaerentes are numerous and obvious. Thus attention has been focused on these junctions since their characteristics in the embryonic tissues of the chick make them particularly useful for experimentation. In most of the cell types studied by the author the gap junctions have been relatively infrequent and inconspicuous as seen in thin sections, and hence they have been largely ignored. Consideration has been given almost entirely to the desmosome.

III. Development of Adhaerens Junctions

A study of desmosome formation in the early embryo and in maturing tissues indicates that these structures characteristically develop symmetrically in adjacent cells, that there is a regular sequence of events leading to the most complex form of these junctions, and that related structures resembling early or mid stages in this developmental process may be characteristic of particular tissues. There is also a typical sequence in which various types of specialized junctions form in embryonic tissues, and study of diseased tissues has revealed a number of abnormalities in desmosome structure and location. Any experimental approach must rest on these findings. Development of desmosomes has been reviewed by Campbell and Campbell (1971) and by Overton (1974).

A. NORMAL DEVELOPMENT

Desmosome formation has been followed in the early embryo and in a number of embryonic tissues. Typically the two halves of the desmosome which lie in different cells have been described as arising simultaneously. Also, in mature tissues the two halves of the desmosome are almost always precisely aligned (Fawcett, 1966). An apparent exception to this rule was noted in developing cornea by Hay and Revel (1969) and later confirmed (Overton, 1973). In this case cells of the corneal epithelium of the chick were studied during stages when an increase in desmosome number was at initial stages. At this time unmatched plaques on lateral cell surfaces were particularly frequent suggesting the interpretation that these single plaques represented stages in desmosome development in which the strictly coordinated activity of the normal process was lacking. As indicated above, unmatched plaques on lateral cell surfaces have also been noted in tumors (Hruban et al., 1972).

Desmosome formation can be broken down into a number of stages, and typically each stage occurs symmetrically in the two adjoining cells. A possible early stage in the process has been noted by Deane and Wurzelmann (1965) in which mitochondria in two opposed cells are aligned with little or no obvious modification of the cytoplasm adjacent to the membrane. The fullest account has been given by Lentz and Trinkaus (1971) as follows: accumulation of dense cytoplasmic material applied to and near the plasma membrane; appearance of intercellular dense material and, at the same time, cytoplasmic fibrils running parallel to and contacting the electron-opaque plaque; widening of the intercellular space; separation of the dense cytoplasmic plaque material from the plasma membrane; increase in compactness of the cytoplasmic plaque; appearance of an intermediate line in the intercellular material; and finally, a more extensive associated system of cytoplasmic filaments which are arranged along lines of stress. This description of desmosome formation in *Fundulus* is generally applicable to many other situations. It has been commonly observed that subsurface densities form first and that an extensive fibrillar system and central stratum appear later. The detailed description of Lentz and Trinkaus (1971) gives some idea of the complexity of the process. In some instances the fully formed junction undergoes subsequent regression, as in the epidermis where there is a typical change in desmosomes between the stratum spinosum and the stratum corneum. In the stratum corneum the cytoplasmic components of the desmosome become less electron dense while the intracellular portion of the junction becomes evenly electron dense with no intermediate layer, but the membrane modification is retained (McNutt, 1973). Finally, with further cornification the desmosomes may be no longer identifiable in sections (see Overton, 1974, for review).

It also appears that many junctions may never reach the mature or complex form. For example, Adams and Whittaker (1972) in comparing human fetal and postnatal skin and oral epithelium note that in the latter tissue a high proportion of "simple" desmosomes which lack the intermediate layer are present even in the most mature stages studied. In addition, a transitory junction termed the primitive desmosome, or macula adhaerens diminuta (Hay, 1968) occurs which consists of small, matched membrane-associated cytoplasmic densities resembling the first stage of desmosome formation. These junctions have generally been considered to be temporary adhesive structures that act at a critical stage in tissue development. Thus desmosomes, through their various developmental and degenerative stages and "simple" as well as "primitive" desmosomes, appear to be a rather closely related group of junctions as judged on the basis of our present information. There has been somewhat less study of the zonulae and fasciae adhaerentes, although observation of developing cardiac muscle suggests that here, as in the case of the desmosome, there is a sequence in which the membrane-associated cytoplasmic density forms first and the fibrils become associated with it later (Huang, 1967).

B. Sequence of Formation of Junctional Types in Development

Studies of early embryonic development indicate that the first cell contacts between migratory cells are focal regions of close contact (Hay, 1968; Trelstad *et al.*, 1967; Lentz and Trinkaus, 1971) followed by larger areas of specialized adhesion. Early focal contacts or gap junctions are associated with electrical coupling and may occur in cleavage stages (for reviews, see Loewenstein, 1973; DeHaan and Sachs, 1972). The first cell contact in tissue culture may form rapidly in as little as 3–4 minutes (Flaxman *et al.*, 1969; DeHaan and Hirakow, 1972) or in some instances even in 20 seconds (Heaysman and Pegrum, 1973). Occluding and intermediate junctions appear next, and only later in stabilized tissue do desmosomes characteristically form (Hay, 1968). Hilfer *et al.* (1968) found junctional complexes in chick thyroid follicle cells after 3 hours of reaggregation. In the embryo, desmosomes seem to develop most rapidly in tissues with certain architectural features. It has been pointed out by Lentz and Trinkaus (1971) that desmosomes may be prominent in epithelial layers stretched by epiboly. In the chick embryo they are not present in the early primitive streak stages but appear in extra embryonic regions in large numbers as the blastoderm enlarges (Balinsky and Walther, 1962; Bellairs, 1963; Overton, 1962; Trelstad *et al.*, 1967), and in *Fundulus* they appear at a time when force is exerted on the epiblast (Lentz and Trinkaus, 1971). A large increase in the frequency of desmosomes has also been correlated with an increasing number of cell layers in stratified epithelium (Hay and Revel, 1969).

C. Abnormal Development

Cancerous cells frequently show changes in their cell surface specializations. Gap junctions which have been studied most extensively are often, though not necessarily, lacking in cancerous tissue (see Loewenstein, 1973, for review), and in some instances occluding junctions have been described as lacking or very rare (e.g., Hruban *et al.*, 1972; Johnson and Sheridan, 1971). Desmosomes, in addition to being reduced or absent (e.g., McNutt and Weinstein, 1970; McNutt *et al.*, 1971) may also be morphologically modified (Hruban *et al.*, 1972; and see Section I). In addition, in keratinocytes of squamous cell carcinomas desmosomes have been observed in intracytoplasmic locations. Von Bülow and Klingmüller (1971) described a keratoacanthoma in which 1–5% of the keratinocytes showed large accumulations of intracytoplasmic desmosomes. Other reports make no estimate of the frequency with which cells show this abnormality. These desmosomes are normal in structure, may be with or without attached tonofilaments and are usually not associated with membrane but in some cases they have been described as vacuolated or with a tennis racket or dumbbell shape. They have been considered as possibly related to Langerhans granules (Caputo and Prandi, 1972), as arising through induction by tonofilaments (Klingmüller *et al.*, 1970) or as resulting from invagination (von Bülow and Klingmüller, 1971; Seiji and Mizuno, 1969). In two reports (Takaki *et al.*, 1971; von Bülow and Klingmüller, 1971) invaginations of the cell membrane in which the two adjacent regions of the surface were joined by a desmosome have been illustrated. Caputo and Prandi (1972) report that they have never observed such images. It is therefore of particular interest that these abnormally located desmosomes should also occur in isolated embryonic cells (see Section V, E).

D. NORMAL DEVELOPMENT OF DESMOSOMES IN SYSTEMS
USED FOR EXPERIMENTS

Two main systems have been used for the study of desmosome formation in the author's laboratory. These are the extra embryonic regions of the 1- to 2-day chick and the corneal epithelium of the late embryo. In each case the normal development of the tissue in question was studied to lay a foundation for experimental work.

The first system studied (Overton, 1962, 1968) was the chick blastoderm between stages 4 and 14 of development (Hamilton, 1952). The regions chosen for study were two lateral strips of the area pellucida immediately outside the main embryonic axis. These regions included all three germ layers, but the differentiating cells of the embryo proper and of the area vasculosa were avoided. In stage 4 (primitive streak) no desmosomes were found. They gradually increased in number and by stage 10 were numerous. By stage 14 they were not only very prominent but were associated with an extensive fibrillar system. Cells at this stage could not be readily dispersed with standard procedures (Moscona, 1961) using calcium-magnesium free Tyrode's and trypsin. Therefore for experimental purposes tissues from stages 7 through 12 were chosen. This material represented diverse types of cells, but desmosomes were present in all three germ layers, although, as described later by Hay (1968) those in the mesoderm were of a less advanced type structurally. The main advantage of this material was that desmosomes were increasing and numerous, yet the tissue was readily dispersed.

Ideally, for study of desmosome formation one would want to use a tissue of uniform cell type at a developmental stage in which desmosomes are forming very rapidly from a known low frequency to a known high frequency. An attempt was made to approach these conditions using the corneal epithelium of the chick. This tissue was chosen partly because the time at which the number of desmosomes begins to increase was known but also because the apparent asymmetry in early stages of the process (Hay and Revel, 1969) seemed an interesting observation that warranted further investigation. A disadvantage of this tissue is that it is composed of morphologically diverse cell types. Of course the basal cells differ from the most apical cells in having hemidesmosomes rather than a free surface with occasional short microvilli, but in addition, cells toward the free surface have a denser cytoplasm containing more fibrils and also they have more desmosomes. For this reason, estimates of the number of desmosomes at any given stage necessitated sampling to include the entire thickness of the epidermis. Samples included micrographs with 50–100 nuclear cross sections, and the number of desmosomes per nuclear cross section was scored. As can be seen from Fig. 1, desmosomes

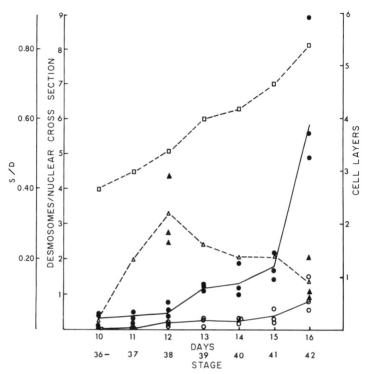

FIG. 1. Desmosome formation in corneal epithelium. ●——●, double plaques; ◯——◯, single plaques; △---△, average ratio of single to double plaques; ▲, on days 12 and 16, individual ratios of single to double plaques—there is no overlap; □---□, average number of cell layers in the epithelium. From Overton (1973), with permission of Rockefeller University Press.

increase in frequency from days 10 through 16 of incubation. There is a conspicuous change in the appearance of the tissue during this time, as illustrated in Figs. 2 and 3. The number of cell layers in the epithelium increases (see Fig. 1), and the appearance of the cytoplasm is altered. Changes in the character of endoplasmic reticulum and increasing density of the cytoplasm are described in detail by Hay and Revel (1969). The increase in number of desmosomes is evident in a comparison of Figs. 2 and 3. There is a gradual increase in desmosome frequency to day 15 (see Fig. 1), followed by a sharp rise to day 16, when the frequency of desmosomes increases about 3-fold over a 24-hour period. There is considerable variation between individual values, but the trend is consistent. Although at best, only 5 or 6 desmosomes per nuclear cross section were recorded, the actual number was far greater because those cut tangentially were not included in the count. The number of single plaques was also recorded, and the proportion was found to be highest in early stages of the process (see Fig. 1), confirming the observations of Hay and Revel (1969). However, later experiments with mixed cells (see Section V, B) indicated that the frequency of these single plaques was not sufficiently high for them to be very useful as a clue to understanding cell interaction.

This preliminary examination of desmosome formation in the cornea indicated that the material would be a suitable system for experimentation if the increase in desmosome frequency between days 15 and 16 could be obtained in culture. Accordingly, counts of desmosomes were made in cultured epithelia and in dispersed and reaggregated epithelial cells (see Table I). These counts showed that essentially the same degree of

TABLE I

DESMOSOMES (DOUBLE PLAQUES)/NUCLEAR CROSS
SECTION IN CORNEAL EPITHELIUM[a]

Number of cases	Treatment	Mean	SD[b]
6	15-Day cornea *in vivo*	1.41	±0.47
5	16-Day cornea *in vivo*	6.44	±1.62
5	15-Day corneal epithelium cultured for 24 hours	5.03	±1.22
5	15-Day corneal epithelium dissociated, pelleted, and cultured for 24 hours	5.72	±1.24
5	10-Day and 15-day corneal epithelium, mixed 50:50, pelleted, and cultured for 24 hours	2.33	±0.88

[a] From Overton (1973), with permission of Rockefeller University Press.
[b] Of the sample.

development of the junctions occurred under culture conditions in epithelial sheets and in reaggregated cells. Therefore this system has been used in further work to study the effects of a drug, cytochalasin B on cell association and cell sorting, and to study the capacity of different sorts of cells to cooperate in junction formation.

There are certain limitations in the use of corneal epithelium for the study of junction development. First, obtaining a sufficient number of cells for a given experiment is relatively time consuming despite the procedures that have been developed for isolating epithelial and mesenchy-

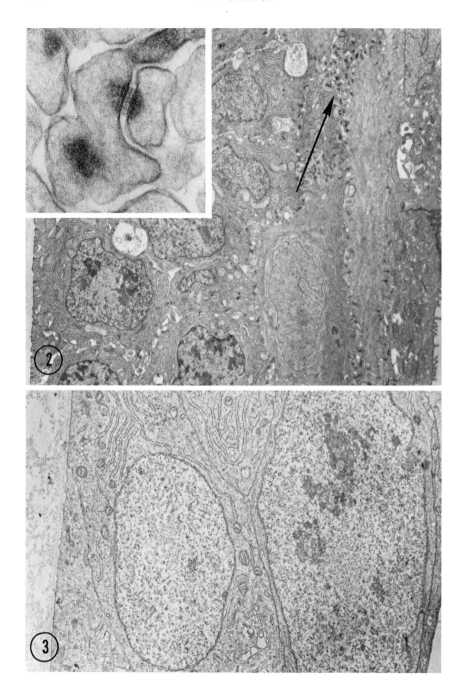

mal corneal components (Dodson and Hay, 1971). Second, the time required for an observable effect and the variation between individual cases are sufficiently great so that this is not an adequate system for analysis by the use of metabolic inhibitors, such as actinomycin D. Third, when epithelial and mesenchymal components are separated, the generative layer of the epithelium is not maintained (Dodson, 1967), hence this system is inappropriate for experimental designs requiring DNA synthesis or cell division. A related limitation which became apparent in the course of further work is that corneal epithelium, like epidermis (Beckingham Smith, 1973), cornifies precociously under culture conditions. As noted in Section III, A, identification of desmosomes is difficult after advanced cornification. This is very rarely a problem with dissociated and reaggregated cells cultured for only 24 hours. Furthermore it can be avoided, since the distribution of junctions and of cell sorting patterns has generally taken on its characteristic form by 16 or 18 hours. In certain circumstances incipient cornification can actually be an advantage, since it can make identification of cell types possible in thick sections stained by routine methods for light microscopy. Thus, although this system cannot be adapted to some kinds of experimental studies, it is admirably suited to others.

IV. Cell Isolation

In studies of junction formation in which the early chick blastoderm was used, desmosomes were frequent in the tissue to be dispersed. A study of the fate of desmosome components after dispersion was essential to understanding junction formation in these reaggregated cells since it was of interest to know whether new junctions formed from partly disrupted components.

The techniques for disruption of tissues preparatory to cell reaggregation depend on treatment with proteolytic enzymes and EDTA. Treatment with these agents causes disappearance of the central lamina and separation of the plaques (Overton, 1962, 1968; Overton and Shoup, 1964; Berry and Friend, 1969; Sedar and Forte, 1964). Zonulae adhaerentes may be similarly affected (Sedar and Forte, 1964) though they are often more resistant. Borysenko and Revel (1973) observed partially dis-

FIG. 2. Corneal epithelium, 16 days of incubation. Arrow indicates cluster of desmosomes. ×6000. Inset, ×75,000. From Overton (1973), with permission of the Rockefeller University Press.

FIG. 3. Corneal epithelium, 10 days of incubation. Epithelium is only 2–3 cell layers thick, desmosomes are scarce, and cytoplasmic characteristics are very different from those of older cells in Fig. 2. ×8000. From Overton (1973), with permission of the Rockefeller University Press.

persed desmosomes and noted rows of toothlike projections adhering to the outer surfaces of junctional unit membranes in cases where junctions were susceptible to disruption by EDTA. When junctions were partially disrupted by trypsin they found loss of the central lamina, or in cases which they interpret as resulting from the enzyme gaining access to the desmosome via the cytoplasmic face of the membrane rather than through the extracellular space, they found images suggestive of slippage of the paired attachment plaques and freeing of the intermediate dense line allowing it to float in the intercellular space. Observations on these very early stages of tissue breakdown which have led to distinctions between desmosome types (see Section II) were overlooked in previous studies of cell dissociation. Once cells have become separated, the intercellular component is lost, but the intracytoplasmic component of the junction remains intact and can be followed readily. When trypsinized cells of the chick blastoderm are dissociated by pipetting after treatment with trypsin (Overton, 1962, 1968), desmosome plaques leave the cell surface. They are withdrawn in association with vacuoles into the central region of the cell (see Fig. 4). These vacuoles initially bear a straight side where

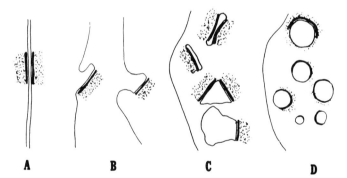

A   **B**   **C**   **D**

FIG. 4. Hypothetical sequence of desmosome engulfment after trypsin treatment. Diagrams are based on micrographs. (A) Normal desmosome; (B) single plaques in cytoplasmic depressions; (C) vacuoles in the cytoplasm associated with plaques; (D) terminal stages of plaque breakdown. From Overton (1968), with permission of the Wistar Press.

the plaque lies with its associated fibrils (Fig. 5). Later, rounded vacuoles are more frequently found. Berry and Friend (1969) described such vacuoles toward the interior of the cell where the width and density of the plaques has become much reduced and fibrils are no longer associated with them. This phenomenon has been observed not only in early chick embryo cells, but also in chick corneal epithelium (Overton and Culver,

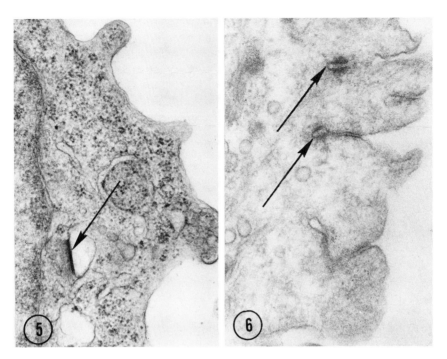

FIG. 5. Cell from the chick blastoderm after trypsinization and dispersion. Arrow, single plaque in vacuole. ×31,000. From Overton (1968), with permission of the Wistar Press.

FIG. 6. Desmosomes located at the terminal end of channels or folds which connect with the cell exterior (arrows). ×60,000. From Overton (1974), with permission of Academic Press.

1973), in rat liver (Berry and Friend, 1969), in chick heart cells (Fischman and Moscona, 1971), in a neoplastic cell culture line (Sträuli et al., 1971), and in a number of epithelia of frog, cat, rat, and human origin (Borysenko and Revel, 1973). In chick embryo and corneal cells this process appears to begin during trypsinization and proceeds rapidly after dispersion. By 2–3 hours of culture desmosomes are no longer characteristic of the cell surface, and those which have become internalized have largely broken down (Overton, 1968; Overton and Culver, 1973). Internalization of desmosome plaques also occurs rapidly during isolation in other tissues (Berry and Friend, 1969; Fischman and Moscona, 1971). The process may be contrasted with cases in which intact desmosomes form at the cell surface and are then taken into the cytoplasm in channels (see Fig. 6 and Section V, E).

Hemidesmosomes on the basal cell surface are also phagocytized and can be distinguished from half-desmosomes on the lateral cell surface since their morphology is distinct (Overton and Culver, 1973). Hemidesmosomes undergo the same process in thyroid-treated amphibian epidermis in culture, where these structures first lose their connections with the basement membrane and then are withdrawn into the cell (Gona, 1970). Therefore it seems possible that engulfment of lateral desmosome plaques in experimentally isolated cells may mimic particular developmental or physiological conditions when normal relationships at the cell surface are changed.

In the course of studies on the relation of cytochalasin B to cell sorting, possible effects of the drug on early stages of cell dissociation were considered (Overton and Culver, 1973). Cytochalasin B has been reported to affect phagocytic activity of the cell surface, inhibiting both endo- and exocytosis (for review, see Overton and Culver, 1973). If cytochalasin B inhibited engulfment of desmosome plaques it would suggest a relation between this process, which may or may not be a normal cell activity, and phagocytosis itself. Treatment of chick corneal cells with the drug did inhibit engulfment of plaques to a very large extent provided it was added to the trypsinizing and rinsing media as well as to the dispersion medium (Overton and Culver, 1973). Figures 7 and 8 illustrate plaques which have been retained at the cell surface. The tonofilaments characteristically remain associated with the plaques. In some cases where cytochalasin B was added to the dissociating medium only, plaques appeared both in vacuoles and on the cell surface. Hemidesmosomes, distinguishable by their distinct morphology (see Section II), were sometimes seen in internal vacuoles.

Desmosomes are extensively associated with systems of tonofilaments and these adhesive sites with their fibrillar attachments have been likened to a system of braces transmitting forces from cell to cell (Mercer, 1965). When cells are disrupted, such forces would be changed and might entail displacement of the plaques. In the presence of cytochalasin B the plaques are not engulfed yet the tonofilaments are not destroyed, so a causal relation between engulfment of plaques and their tonofilament connections seems unlikely. Engulfment of the plagues presumably results from the same types of surface movement as endocytosis.

In cytochalasin B-treated cells, desmosomes that have been disrupted remain at the cell surface with their fibrillar connections both in isolated cells and also, apparently, after these cells have been reaggregated. Although no quantitative studies have been made of the phenomenon, there often seem to be an unusually large number of single plaques in cytochalasin B-treated aggregates after 24 hours of culture in the presence

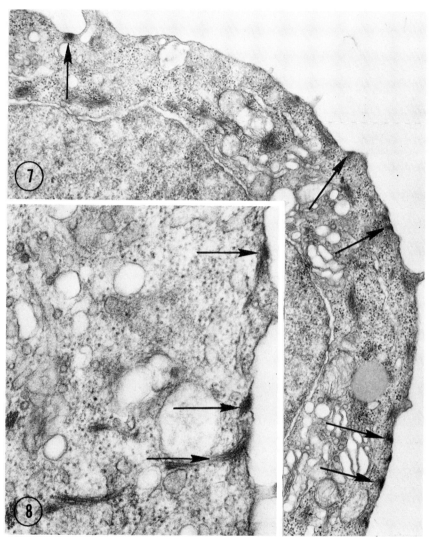

Figs. 7 and 8. Corneal cells dispersed in cytochalasin B. Arrows indicate desmosome components which remain at the cell surface. Fig. 7, ×23,000; Fig. 8, ×39,000. From Overton and Culver (1973), both figures with permission of the Wistar Press.

of the drug. Since single plaques occur in normal development in corneal epithelium (see Section III, D), it is difficult to determine the source of these plaques with certainty.

These studies indicate that trypsinized cells from a number of tissues as prepared for reaggregation studies show a rapid and possibly a selective removal of certain adhesive sites on the cell surface. Therefore new adhesive sites must be formed during aggregation.

V. Cell Recombination

Desmosome formation in the course of cell reaggregation has been studied in combinations of like and of unlike cells. As indicated in Section III, dispersed corneal cells, when reassociated, form desmosomes with the normal frequency. This system has been used to inquire into the capabilities of different cell types to form junctions with each other and into the possible relationship between these capabilities and cell sorting behavior. The drug cytochalasin B has been shown by a number of investigators to inhibit cell sorting (Sanger and Holtzer, 1972; Maslow and Mayhew, 1972; Armstrong and Parenti, 1972; Steinberg and Wiseman, 1972). It therefore seemed important to know whether it might affect formation of cell surface adhesive sites. If it did not, it was thought that the drug might be useful in preventing experimentally mixed cells from sorting and hence could be used to allow surface interactions to take place which would otherwise be prevented by segregation of the cells.

A. DESMOSOME FORMATION IN THE PRESENCE OF CYTOCHALASIN B

Treatment of pellets of dissociated 15-day corneal cells with cytochalasin B at dosages of 3–10 μg/ml appeared to delay the process of close cell apposition. However, by 24 hours of culture, extensive areas of cell surface had become closely apposed and numerous desmosomes had formed. This was also true if the drug was added 2 hours after dissociation to ensure that any original desmosome components had broken down. These junctions appeared by morphological criteria to be entirely normal (Overton and Culver, 1973). Previous studies of aggregation in the presence of cytochalasin B has shown that in most cases cell sorting was abolished in dosages such as those used here which were sufficient to inhibit cell locomotion on a solid substrate (Armstrong and Parenti, 1972; Steinberg and Wiseman, 1972). In one interesting exception in which pigmented retina and neural retina were combined, a remarkable amount of sorting took place (Armstrong and Parenti, 1972). The view has been put forward that when such sorting does occur it may be explained as due not to active cell movement, but to adhesive forces between like cell surfaces which draw the cells together (Armstrong and Parenti, 1972; Steinberg and Wiseman, 1972). According to this view, corneal cells which form many junctions and extensive areas of surface apposition in the presence of the drug should show at least partial sorting. This was in fact the case (see Section V, C).

B. LOCAL EFFECTS OF FOREIGN CELLS ON DESMOSOME FORMATION

When corneal cells are mixed in pellets with cells of other types, although there is cell sorting, in some regions of the pellet corneal and foreign cells lie next to each other and under these circumstances interaction between two diverse cell types can be studied. In appropriate sections a corneal cell may lie next to other corneal cells on some parts of its surface and next to a foreign cell elsewhere. In comparing these two parts of the same cell surface one can determine the effects of different local environments on desmosome formation (Overton, 1973). Corneal cells of 15 days' incubation have been juxtaposed in pellets with pigmented retina cells. Pigmented retina has no desmosomes (Armstrong, 1971) but does have prominent junctions of the intermediate type. Corneal cells which are forming desmosomes rapidly have also been mixed with 10-day corneal cells which make few if any desmosomes over the succeeding 24-hour period (see Fig. 1). In an experiment of this kind cell identification is crucial. Pigment granules provide an unambiguous marker and, in pigmented retina from chicks of 10 days' incubation, granules are typically widely distributed throughout the cytoplasm. In the case of 10- and 15-day corneal cells, there are distinct differences in the cytoplasm, particularly in the conformation of the endoplasmic reticulum. This makes it possible to identify some corneal cells from each source, though not every cell can be identified. Micrographs were obtained of regions of the pellets of mixed cells in which 15-day corneal cells made contact with foreign cells. Such a region is illustrated in Figure 9. The length of the 15-day corneal cell surface as seen in cross section was measured in micrometers, and the number of desmosomes associated with the membrane next to like or unlike cells was counted. When the frequencies of desmosomes on different surfaces of the same 15-day cell are compared (see Table II), it is evident that on those parts of the surface which lie next to a foreign cell, desmosomes are scarce or lacking. Calculations indicate that, at the same time, on other parts of the same cell surface where like cells are adjacent desmosomes occur with approximately their normal frequency (Overton, 1973). Thus in these cases local conditions at the cell surface determine whether or not a desmosome will form. A cell that does not form these junctions can suppress them in a cell which does, and a younger cell cannot in this instance be stimulated to form desmosomes at a time when it would not normally form them. These findings are consistent with, but go beyond, the data obtained by counting the number of desmosomes per nuclear cross section in a pellet of mixed cells (see Table I, last entry).

This observation that strictly local conditions at the cell surface are operative in desmosome formation is shown experimentally in the studies

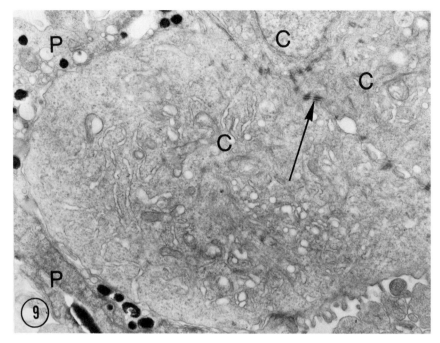

Fig. 9. Aggregate of pigmented epithelium (P) and corneal cells (C). Arrow indicates desmosome between corneal cells. ×11,000.

TABLE II

Desmosome Frequency on Different Sides of the Same 16-Day Corneal Epithelial Cell[a]

Cell types combined	Number of cells	Micrometers/desmosome, double plaques		Number of single plaques observed	
		Side A (same cell type)	Side B (different cell type)	Side A	Side B
10- and 15-Day corneal epithelium	50	2.04	25.1	1	6
15-Day corneal epithelium and pigmented retina	50	1.75	35.0	3	1

[a] From Overton (1973), with permission of Rockefeller University Press.

just described, but the phenomenon was also noted previously in connection with examination of normal tissues. One of the most clear-cut examples is illustrated by Breathnach and Wyllie (1967) in the epidermis. Here Langerhans cells, which characteristically lack desmosomes, lie in the stratum spinosum, where desmosomes are numerous. Cells of the stratum spinosum show an abrupt change on those parts of their surfaces that lie next to Langerhans cells. Here local inhibition of desmosomes is evident.

Although nothing is known about the synthesis of the components of desmosomes, it seems possible that local inhibition of this kind is an inhibition of assembly, since desmosomes in other regions of the surface of the same cell form with their normal frequency.

C. SELECTIVE DESMOSOME FORMATION

There are many cases in which different cells which normally lie adjacent within a given tissue form junctions with each other (Armstrong, 1970; Overton, 1974). Experiments described in Section V, B imply that in some cases cells are more selective in the junctions which they will form. The corneal epithelium seemed to be good material to test this suggestion with regard to desmosomes. Cytoplasmic markers are the most satisfactory, and in experiments to date pigment granules, muscle fibers, and the distinctive mitochondria of liver have been used (Overton, 1974b). Corneal cells have been combined with cells that form desmosomes and those which do not and the capability of these combinations of cells to form junctions of the intermediate type as well as desmosomes has been noted. Fifteen-day corneal cells were combined with 7-day chick heart ventricle in which both desmosomes and fasciae adhaerentes are common, and with 7-day pigmented retina cells in which junctions of the intermediate type occur, but where desmosomes are lacking (Armstrong, 1971). In addition, some experiments have been carried out using liver of the quail *Corturnix japonica*. In these experiments dispersed mixed cells were reaggregated in rotating culture after the method of Moscona (1961), and the patterns of aggregation were noted.

In combinations of heart and cornea, by 24 hours or less cell segregation was evident (Overton, 1974b). Spheres of corneal and muscle cells could be distinguished in living preparations. Aggregates of the two cell types were occasionally completely separated, but more commonly they adhered by restricted regions of the surface like the diagrams of Steinberg (1963) depicting two cell types in which each has a greater affinity for its own type than for the other. Typically, a heart aggregate had one or several small corneal aggregates attached to it. Examination of cell surfaces showed that corneal cells formed many desmosomes among themselves as well as zonulae or fasciae adhaerentes in restricted regions, while heart cells formed many desmosomes and fasciae adhaerentes with other heart cells. Where heart and corneal cells were adjacent, only junctions of the fascia adhaerens type were observed (Fig. 10). Since relatively few regions in the culture showed juxtaposition of cells from different sources, an attempt was made to increase the number of such cell contacts by treatment with cytochalasin B (see Section V, A). The drug

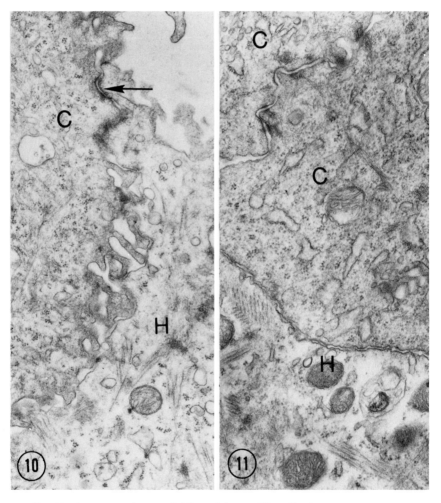

FIG. 10. Aggregate of corneal (C) and heart (H) cells. Arrow, intermediate junction between heart and corneal cells. ×20,000.

FIG. 11. Aggregate of corneal (C) and heart (H) cells. Desmosomes are present between corneal cells, but not between heart and cornea. ×18,000.

did not abolish cell sorting between heart and corneal cells but did modify and reduce it (see Section V, D). In treated aggregates the types of junctions which formed remained the same. In a typical field, corneal cells formed numerous desmosomes with other corneal cells whereas on surfaces adjacent to heart cells these junctions were absent (Fig. 11). In rare cases, both corneal and muscle cells showed subsurface densities of a local type associated with a part of the membrane where the two cell types were opposed, but these densities were not matched by the opposite cell. In only two instances images which might be interpreted as abortive desmosome formation were seen. In these cases a single plaque in muscle was matched in the corneal cell by an ill-defined subsurface density. Except for these two isolated instances desmosomes between cornea and muscle were absent, and in view of their very numerous occurrence elsewhere it seems safe to conclude that they are virtually absent between muscle and cornea.

In parallel experiments with pigmented retina, desmosomes formed exclusively between corneal cells, yet junctions of the intermediate type occurred between unlike cells. These zonulae or fasciae adhaerentes are readily recognizable in most instances. Occasionally such junctions may have a macular appearance, possibly due to the plane of the section or to their developmental state, but such regions never have a central stratum, clearly defined plaques, or associated 100 Å filaments, all of which are characteristic of the mature desmosome or macula adhaerens. Only zonulae or fasciae adhaerentes form between cornea and liver (Overton, 1974b) as images of these junctions are defined here and between pigmented retina and heart muscle (Armstrong, 1970). Junctions of the intermediate type likewise occur between pigmented and neural retina (Armstrong, 1971). Thus cornea forms junctions of the intermediate type with three other cell types with which it will not form desmosomes, and pigmented retina forms intermediate junctions with three other cell types. Although this evidence is very fragmentary it suggests at the present time that desmosomes may be more selective than intermediate junctions. As cells differentiate in a developing embryo, perhaps those junctions that form early (see Section II, B) are more similar and widespread whereas those that form last are the most selective. Trelstad et al. (1967) have also suggested, on the basis of a detailed study of the early chick embryo, that certain junctions, particularly those such as focal tight or gap junctions which occur very early, are less selective. Of course it is also true that some cells may finally become specialized in a way that eliminates gap junctions (see DeHaan and Hirakow, 1972).

As noted in the Introduction, new distinctions between junctions continue to be made, and it has been emphasized that any junction must be studied by a number of complementary techniques in order to be fully characterized (McNutt and Weinstein, 1973; Johnson and Sheridan, 1971). Perhaps biochemical differences between desmosomes from different sources as suggested by Borysenko and Revel (1973) might account for the selectivity that appears to exist in desmosome formation. On the other hand, there are no experiments to date which would require this explanation. Any further studies that might suggest biochemical identity between junctions from different sources could be complemented by a test of whether the cells of origin would form normal junctions when confronted.

D. CELL SORTING AND JUNCTION FORMATION

Experiments carried out to date show no simple relationship between junction formation and cell sorting. However, they do suggest that under some circumstances junctions might contribute to the sorting process as has been postulated by Trelstad et al. (1967) on the basis of study of the fine structure of the early chick embryo. If desmosome formation alone is considered, one might expect 15-day corneal cells to sort rapidly since they form numerous adhesive sites between cell surfaces over a relatively short period of time. Cytochalasin B in dosages that inhibit movement of many cells on a solid substrate will also usually inhibit cell sorting. In one instance, a remarkable amount of sorting has been reported (Armstrong and Parenti, 1972), and it was suggested that this could result from passive movement of cells due to adhesive forces between like cell surfaces (Armstrong and Parenti, 1972; Steinberg and Wiseman, 1972). Desmosome formation between corneal cells occurs in comparable dosages of cytochalasin B, and extensive close apposition of surfaces is apparent by 24 hours of culture. In the case of these corneal cells "passive movement" due to "zipping up" of adhesive cell surfaces might therefore be expected. Actually, corneal cells did show considerable segregation in dosages of 3–5 μg of cytochalasin B when mixed with either heart, liver, or pigmented retina. Although corneal cells formed discrete rounded aggregates under these conditions, there was much more extensive contact with foreign cells then in the absence of the drug. For example, in the presence of cytochalasin B, heart cells typically surrounded and held together a number of spheres of corneal cells, whereas in normal medium the two cell types were largely or sometimes completely separated. The drug treatment was reversible to a considerable extent (see Figs. 12–15).

In all the cell combinations that were made, desmosomes formed selectively between corneal cells, which is consistent with the sorting pattern. However, intermediate junctions were not selective. In normal culture medium a sphere of muscle cells may remain attached to a sphere of

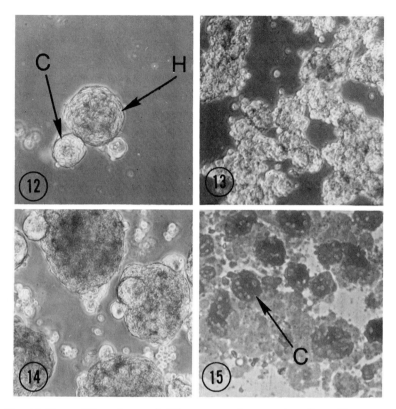

FIG. 12. Heart (H) and corneal (C) aggregate in normal medium. The two types of cells adhere in limited regions. Living preparation, phase contrast. ×120.

FIG. 13. Heart and corneal aggregate, cultured in cytochalasin B, 5 μg/ml. Living preparation, phase contrast. ×120.

FIG. 14. Heart and corneal aggregate, after 24 hours' recovery from cytochalasin B treatment. ×120.

FIG. 15. Thick section of cytochalasin B-treated culture like that shown in Fig. 13. Arrow, spherical aggregate of corneal cells which has sorted from heart cells. ×120.

corneal cells joined by fasciae or zonulae adhaerentes between the two different cell types. We know that these junctions can form relatively rapidly (see Section III, B), so the reason why they do not form early and prevent sorting must be sought. Perhaps these junctions form when cell movement has become reduced (Hay, 1968). In the case of pigmented and neural retina described by Armstrong (1971) sorting occurs although junctions of the intermediate type can occur between pigmented retina cells, between neural retina cells, and between these two different kinds of cells as well. One might invoke quantitative differences to explain sort-

ing in this instance (see Steinberg, 1963), but so little is known about
the frequency of intermediate junctions, or of the other junctions that
occur in this system, that the relation between junction formation and
cell sorting is made no clearer. Although the situation is obviously complex, at least it can be said that selective adhesion between cells occurs,
and that desmosomes are certainly adhesive and also selective in the tissue studied here. Understanding of the question may be advanced when
it becomes possible to study the spatial distribution of tissue-specific
aggregation factors (e.g., Garber and Moscona, 1972; Humphreys, 1963;
Pessac and Defendi, 1972; Müller and Zahn, 1973) on the cell surface.
Loewenstein (1967) has shown that this factor in sponges contributes to
cell coupling, and thus presumably to a specialized surface modification.

E. Junctions between Regions on the Same Cell Surface

Desmosomes between two parts of the same cell surface have been
seen in reaggregates of 15-day corneal cells (Overton and Culver, 1973),
but they are rare. They occur when cells are reaggregated in the presence
of cytochalasin B, but this is also a rare occurrence. The phenomenon
is more frequent when corneal and pigmented retina cells are mixed and
treated with cytochalasin B to inhibit or reduce segregation. In these
preparations, as well as those untreated with the drug, this abnormal
location of desmosomes occurs most frequently where the two cell types
are adjacent. When corneal and pigment cells are opposed, by far the
most typical result is a lack of desmosomes on adjacent cell surfaces
(see Section V, B and C) but under the appropriate experimental conditions these abnormal junctions are sufficiently frequent so that one may
select a series of cases that form a reasonable if hypothetical sequence
depicting their formation and fate (Overton, 1974b). Such a sequence
is as follows: The desmosome forms first at the surface in a shallow indentation of the membrane, so that a section normal to the cell surface
shows the long axis of the desmosome as seen in section pointing toward
the interior of the cell. These desmosomes may or may not be complete
with central stratum binding the two sides of the indentation together.
The desmosome then moves inward, remaining connected with the exterior by a long groove or channel, which typically has a width of about
200 Å or approximately the same distance found between closely apposed
cells. Additional desmosomes may form in this channel behind the first.
The terminal desmosome will eventually become separated from the
channel and float freely in the cytoplasm, carrying with it a minimal
amount of membrane (see Fig. 16). This process is unlike the engulfment
of single plaques after trypsinization of cells since in the latter case single
plaques are typically associated with membranous vesicles, and though

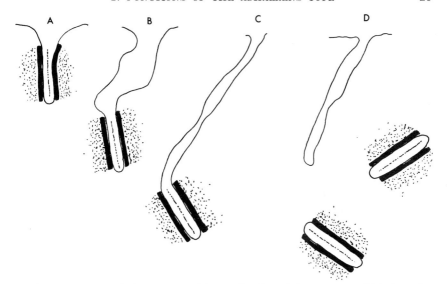

FIG. 16. Hypothetical sequence of internalization of desmosomes which form between two parts of the surface of the same cell. Diagrams are based on micrographs. A desmosome forms near the surface (A), the channel or fold elongates (B) and (C), and finally the desmosome breaks free (D).

two or more such plaques are occasionally associated with the same vesicle, they rarely lie parallel to one another, and in no case is a central stratum evident. This hypothetical sequence of abnormal junction formation is similar to the process which has been postulated to occur in certain tumors (see Section III, C) to explain clusters of desmosomes which lie free in the cytoplasm. Sections showing other elongated junctions possibly of the gap or intermediate type occasionally occur with a similar orientation to abnormal desmosomes; one end attached to the membrane lying at the cell surface and the other pointing toward the interior of the cell. Channels may also occur with the usual terminal desmosome followed by intermediate or possible gap or occluding junctions.

Abnormally located junctions have been seen in cell aggregates of 18–24 hours of culture. This surface activity can presumably be observed with the present degree of detail because the corneal cells that display it are between 15 and 16 days of incubation at a stage when desmosomes form rapidly and are numerous. When cells of this sort are adjacent to foreign cells locally (see Sections V, B and C) inhibition of junction formation occurs, so perhaps it is an extensive juxtaposition with foreign cells which in some way precipitates the formation of junctions in an abnormal position. An initial irregularity in the cell surface could act as a site of desmosome formation, which might move inward as the two adjacent parts of the cell surface continued a "zipper" action. This is only one of a number of possible explanations. However, any satisfactory interpretation must account for the fact that the desmosome typically lies at the extreme inner end of a narrow fold or channel in the cell surface. Although there is some evidence that cytochalasin B reduces surface mobility in these cells in the sense that processes analogous to phagocytosis are reduced or inhibited (see Section I, V), in certain instances (Bluemink and De Laat, 1973) surface movement continues in the presence of cytochalasin B, and such movement could permit irregularities in contour to arise. Such irregularities could then result in sites favorable for the initiation of desmosome formation, despite the fact that cell motility may have been reduced.

Desmosomes and other organized surface junctions occur between different parts of the same cell surface in normal cells. For example, in vertebrates there is a stacked series of desmosomes in the Schwann sheath (Hama, 1959), the two arms of the socket cell show a surface modification where they meet at the base of an insect scale (Overton, 1966), and in certain tripanosomatid flagellates the base of the flagellum is bound to the wall of the flagellar pocket by desmosomes (Brooker, 1970). We know that the site of desmosome formation can be determined by local changes at the cell surface (see Section V, B). Proximity of appropriate surfaces is an obvious necessity, but this alone does not readily explain the regular and varied arrangements of desmosomes which exist (see Section I).

Desmosomes as well as other sites on the membrane may be spaced in accordance with the molecular organization of the cytoplasm. Certain sites, for example, may be associated with protein that penetrates the lipid bilayer (Marchesi, 1972) or with cytoplasmic microtubules (Yahara and Edelman, 1973). Evidence for translational movement of membrane components is accumulating from a variety of experimental approaches and is also strongly suggested by study of junction formation (see Overton, 1974). Drifting of intramembranous particles to become gradually associated in specific geometric arrays as junctions increase in size and take on their mature conformation is implied by freeze-cleave studies, particularly those of developing septate junctions (Gilula, 1972) and gap and occluding junctions (Yee, 1972). Desmosomes (Lentz and Trinkaus, 1971) and hemidesmosomes (Kelly and Shienvold, 1973) also start as small patches that enlarge. The mature conformation of the membrane is achieved in association with cytoplasmic, but also with external, conditions (see Section V). Eventually it might be possible to manipulate this pattern not only environmentally but also by genetic means, since in the case of gap junctions (Loewenstein, 1973; Larsen et al., 1973) a genetic approach to the study of junction formation has been initiated.

VI. Summary

Early experiments involving cell dissociation suggested that cells might have certain affinities, and later work demonstrated selective grouping of cells. The present task is to understand the relation between this behavior and the organization of the cell membrane. The approach taken in this review is that the capacity of cells to form certain well recognized adhesive sites or to remove these sites from the surface and the conditions under which they will do so is a cell behavior study in itself. More information at the molecular level will complement and extend this kind of work. Of particular interest in this connection should be future studies concerning the degree to which junction formation can be viewed as a process of self assembly and studies relating aggregation factors to the topography of the cell surface.

Most if not all specialized surface junctions as well as the rest of the cell membrane contribute to adhesion, and we have no way of knowing at present the relative contributions of each. A study of the formation of adhaerens junctions concentrates on only one limited part of the problem, but has the advantage that these junctions are often related to the organization of the interior of the cell in an obvious way and thus in favorable cases may permit study of cell as well as tissue organization. The corneal epithelium of the chick is suitable material for work on desmosome development because at a given stage there is a marked increase in junction formation over a relatively short period. Some questions which may be addressed are the following: Can one cell stimulate or inhibit junction formation in another locally or generally? How selective is junction formation? What promotes or inhibits junction formation between two parts of the same cell surface? Eventually a set of valid statements concerning such cell surface interactions may be devised.

REFERENCES

Adams, D., and Whittaker, D. K. (1972). *Micron* 3, 186.
Armstrong, P. B. (1970). *J. Cell Biol.* 47, 197.
Armstrong, P. B. (1971). *Wilhelm Roux' Arch. Entwicklungsmech. Organismen* 168, 125.
Armstrong, P. B., and Parenti, D. (1972). *J. Cell Biol.* 55, 542.
Balinsky, B. I., and Walther, H. (1962). *Acta Embryol. Morphol. Exp.* 4, 261.
Bellairs, R. (1963). *J. Embryol. Exp. Morphol.* 11, 201.
Beckingham Smith, K. (1973). *Develop. Biol.* 30, 263.
Benedetti, E. L., and Emmelot, P. (1967). *J. Cell Sci.* 2, 499.
Berry, M. N., and Friend, D. S. (1969). *J. Cell Biol.* 43, 506.
Bluemink, J. G., and De Laat, S. W. (1973). *J. Cell Biol.* 59, 89.

Borysenko, J. Z., and Revel, J.-P. (1973). *Amer. J. Anat.* **137**, 403.

Breathnach, A., and Wyllie, M.-A. (1967). *Advan. Biol. Skin* **8**, 97–113.

Breathnach, A. S., Goodman, T., Stolinsky, C., and Gross, M. (1972a). *J. Anat.* **113**, 291.

Breathnach, A. S., Stolinsky, C., and Gross, M. (1972b). *Micron* **3**, 287.

Brody, I. (1968). *Acta Dermato-Venereol.* **48**, 290.

Brooker, B. E. (1970). *Z. Zellforsch. Mikrosk. Anat.* **105**, 155.

Campbell, R. D., and Campbell, J. H. (1971). In "Origin and Continuity of Cell Organelles" (J. Reinert and H. Ursprung, eds.), pp. 261–298. Springer-Verlag, Berlin and New York.

Caputo, R., and Prandi, G. (1972). *J. Ultrastruct. Res.* **41**, 358.

Clément, P., and Fouillet, X. (1970). In "Microscopie Electronique, 1970" (P. Favard, ed.), Vol. III, pp. 7–8.

Deane, H. W., and Wurzelmann, S. (1965). *Amer. J. Anat.* **117**, 91.

DeHaan, R. L., and Hirakow, R. (1972). *Exp. Cell Res.* **70**, 214.

DeHaan, R. L., and Sachs, H. G. (1972). *Curr. Top. Develop. Biol.* **7**, 193–228.

Dodson, J. W. (1967). *J. Embryol. Exp. Morphol.* **17**, 83.

Dodson, J. W., and Hay, E. D. (1971). *Exp. Cell Res.* **65**, 215.

Douglas, W. H., Ripley, R. C., and Ellis, R. A. (1970). *J. Cell Biol.* **44**, 211.

Farquhar, M. G., and Palade, G. E. (1963). *J. Cell Biol.* **17**, 375.

Fawcett, D. W. (1966). "An Atlas of Fine Structure, The Cell." Saunders, Philadelphia, Pennsylvania.

Fawcett, D. W., and McNutt, N. S. (1969). *J. Cell Biol.* **42**, 1.

Fischman, D., and Moscona, A. A. (1971). In "Cardiac Hypertrophy" (N. Alpert, ed.), pp. 125–139. Academic Press, New York.

Flaxman, B. A., Revel, J.-P., and Hay, E. D. (1969). *Exp. Cell Res.* **58**, 438.

Friend, D. S., and Gilula, N. B. (1972). *J. Cell Biol.* **53**, 758.

Garber, B. B., and Moscona, A. A. (1972). *Develop. Biol.* **27**, 235.

Gilula, N. (1972). *J. Cell Biol.* **55**, 86a.

Gona, A. G. (1970). *J. Ultrastruct. Res.* **30**, 103.

Goodenough, D. A., and Stoeckenius, W. (1972). *J. Cell Biol.* **54**, 646.

Hama, K. (1959). *J. Biophys. Biochem. Cytol.* **6**, 61.

Hamilton, H. L. (1952). "Lillie's Development of the Chick." Holt, New York.

Hay, E. (1968). In "Epithelial-Mesenchymal Interactions" (R. Fleischmajer and R. E. Billingham, eds.), pp. 31–55. Williams & Wilkins, Baltimore, Maryland.

Hay, E., and Revel, J.-P. (1969). "Fine Structure of Developing Avian Cornea." Karger, Basel.

Heaysman, J. E., and Pegrum, S. M. (1973). *Exp. Cell Res.* **78**, 71.

Hilfer, S. R., Izzard, L. B., and Hilfer, E. K. (1968). *Z. Zellforsch. Mikrosk. Anat.* **92**, 256.

Hruban, Z., Mochizuki, Y., Slesers, A., and Morris, H. P. (1972). *Cancer Res.* **32**, 853.

Huang, C. Y. (1967). *J Ultrastruct. Res.* **20**, 211.

Humphreys, T. (1963). *Develop. Biol.* **8**, 27.

Ishikawa, H., Bischoff, R., and Holtzer, H. (1969). *J. Cell Biol.* **43**, 312.

Jessen, H. (1970). *J. Ultrastruct. Res.* **33**, 95.

Johnson, R. G., and Sheridan, J. D. (1971). *Science* **174**, 717.

Joyon, L., Malet, P., and Turchini, J. P. (1964). *C. R. Acad. Sci.* **259**, 2532.

Karnovsky, M. J., and Unanue, E. R. (1973). *Fed. Proc., Fed. Amer. Soc. Exp. Biol.* **32**, 55.

Kelly, D. E. (1966). J. Cell Biol. 28, 51.
Kelly, D. E., and Shienvold, F. (1973). J. Cell Biol. 59, 166a.
Klingmüller, G., Klehr, H. U., and Ishibashi, Y. (1970). Arch. Klin. Exp. Dermatol. 238, 356.
Larsen, W., Azarnia, R., and Loewenstein, W. R. (1973). J. Cell Biol. 59, 186a.
Lentz, T. L., and Trinkaus, J. P. (1971). J. Cell Biol. 48, 455.
Levi, C., and Porte, A. (1964). Z. Zellforsch. Mikrosk. Anat. 62, 293.
Loewenstein, W. R. (1967). Develop. Biol. 15, 503.
Loewenstein, W. R. (1973). Fed. Proc., Fed. Amer. Soc. Biol. 32, 60.
McNutt, N. S. (1970). Amer. J. Cardiol. 25, 169.
McNutt, N. S. (1973). J. Cell Biol. 59, 210a.
McNutt, N. S., and Weinstein, R. S. (1969). Science 165, 597.
McNutt, N. S., and Weinstein, R. S. (1970). J. Cell Biol. 47, 666.
McNutt, N. S., and Weinstein, R. S. (1973). Prog. Biophys. Mol. Biol. 26, 47-101.
McNutt, N. S., Hershberg, R. A., and Weinstein, R. S. (1971). J. Cell Biol. 51, 805.
Marchesi, V. T., Tillack, T. W., Jackson, R. L., Segrest, J. P., and Scott, R. E. (1972). Proc. Nat. Acad. Sci. U.S. 69, 1445.
Maslow, D. E., and Mayhew, E. (1972). Science 177, 281.
Mercer, E. H. (1965). In "Organogenesis" (R. L. DeHaan and H. Ursprung, eds.), pp. 29-54. Holt, New York.
Moscona, A. A. (1960). In "Developing Cell Systems and their Control" (D. Rudnick, ed.), pp. 45-70. Ronald Press, New York.
Moscona, A. A. (1961). Exp. Cell Res. 22, 455.
Müller, W. E. G., and Zahn, R. K. (1963). Exp. Cell Res. 80, 95.
Noirot-Timothée, C., and Noirot, C. (1967). J. Miscrosc. (Paris) 6, 87.
Overton, J. (1962). Develop. Biol. 4, 532.
Overton, J. (1966). J. Cell Biol. 29, 293.
Overton, J. (1968). J. Exp. Zool. 168, 203.
Overton, J. (1973). J. Cell Biol. 56, 636.
Overton, J. (1974a). Prog. Surface Sci. Membrane Sci. 8, 161-208.
Overton, J. (1974b). Develop. Biol. 39, 210.
Overton, J., and Culver, N. (1973). J. Exp. Zool. 185, 341.
Overton, J., and Shoup, J. (1964). J. Cell Biol. 21, 75.
Pardee, A. B. (1971). In Vitro 7, 95.
Pessac, B., and Defendi, V. (1972). Nature (London), New Biol. 238, 13.
Raff, M. C., and De Petris, S. (1973). Fed. Proc., Fed. Amer. Soc. Exp. Biol. 32, 48.
Rambourg, A., and Leblond, C. P. (1967). J. Cell Biol. 32, 27.
Rayns, D. G., Simpson, F. O., and Ledingham, J. M. (1969). J. Cell Biol. 42, 322.
Revel, J.-P., Yee, A. G., and Hudspeth, A. J. (1971). Proc. Nat. Acad. Sci. U.S. 68, 2924.
Rosenblith, J. Z., and Revel, J.-P. (1972). Anat. Rec. 172, 394.
Sanger, J. W., and Holtzer, H. (1972). Proc. Nat. Acad. Sci. U.S. 69, 253.
Sedar, A. W., and Forte, J. G. (1964). J. Cell Biol. 22, 173.
Seiji, M., and Mizuno, F. (1969). Arch. Dermatol. 99, 3.
Singer, S. J., and Nicolson, G. L. (1972). Science 175, 720.
Smith, S. B., and Revel, J.-P. (1973). Develop. Biol. 27, 434.
Staehelin, L. A., Mukherjee, T. M., and Williams, A. W. (1969). Protoplasma 67, 165.

Steinberg, M. (1962). *Proc. Nat. Acad. Sci. U.S.* **48,** 1769.

Steinberg, M. S. (1963). *Science* **141,** 401.

Steinberg, M. S., and Wiseman, L. L. (1972). *J. Cell Biol.* **55,** 606.

Sträuli, P., Lindemann, R., and Haemmerli, G. (1971). *Virchows Arch., B* **8,** 143.

Szabo, T., and Wersäll, J. (1970). *J. Ultrastruct. Res.* **30,** 473.

Takaki, Y., Masutani, M., and Kawada, A. (1971). *Acta Dermato-Venereol.* **51,** 21.

Tandler, B., and Hoppel, C. L. (1970). *Z. Zellforsch. Mikrosk. Anat.* **110,** 166.

Trelstad, R. L., Hay, E. D., and Revel, J.-P. (1967). *Develop. Biol.* **16,** 78.

von Bülow, M., and Klingmüller, G. (1971). *Arch. Dermatol. Forsch.* **241,** 292.

Whitten, J. M. (1973). *Science* **181,** 1066.

Wolff, K., and Schreiner, E. (1971). *J. Ultrastruct. Res.* **36,** 437.

Yahara, I., and Edelman, G. M. (1973). *Nature (London)* **246,** 152.

Yee, A. (1972). *J. Cell Biol.* **55,** 294a.

CHAPTER 2

THE EXTRACELLULAR MATRIX: A DYNAMIC COMPONENT OF THE DEVELOPING EMBRYO

Francis J. Manasek

DEPARTMENTS OF CARDIOLOGY AND PATHOLOGY, THE CHILDREN'S HOSPITAL
MEDICAL CENTER AND DEPARTMENT OF ANATOMY, HARVARD MEDICAL
SCHOOL, BOSTON, MASSACHUSETTS; AND DEPARTMENT OF ANATOMY,
THE UNIVERSITY OF CHICAGO, CHICAGO, ILLINOIS

I. General Considerations of Extracellular Matrix

Mature tissues and organs are functionally integrated units that consist of both cellular and extracellular elements. Cells are in intimate association with the contents of the extracellular regions, and the latter form the immediate environment within which cells perform their various functions. Extracellular regions contain a variety of substances including macromolecules, water, and ions. Collectively these substituents form the *extracellular matrix.*

Extracellular matrices exhibit a great deal of quantitative variation among different tissues. For example, tendon, a dense connective tissue, has a large extracellular compartment (collagen) and a relatively small cellular compartment (tendon cells). On the other hand, a tissue such as liver is principally cellular and the extracellular compartment is relatively small. In addition to the quantitative size differences, the extracellular matrices of different tissues exhibit markedly different compositions. Hyaline cartilage, for example, contains nearly equal amounts of sulfated glycosaminoglycans and collagen. Tendon contains largely collagen whereas bone contains, in addition, large amount of inorganic hydroxyapatite mineral. Thus, parenchymal cells of different tissues are exposed to environments that are markedly different.

The macromolecules of the extracellular matrix, for example, glycosaminoglycans, collagen, and glycoproteins, are all cell products. Macromolecular composition to a large extent determines degree of hydration, ionic composition, permeability, and mechanical properties of different extracellular matrices.

MATRIX AS THE CELLULAR ENVIRONMENT

Cells resident in, or in contact with, extracellular matrix have in many instances the ability to regulate one or more properties of their environment and in turn be influenced by the changed environment. Thus it can be envisioned that one tissue may affect an adjacent tissue by subtle modulation of one or more of many possible variables defining such a dynamic multicomponent equilibrium.

1. The Milieu Interieur

The regulated maintenance of the cellular environment is one of the cornerstone concepts in physiology. Claude Bernard in his concept of the milieu interieur pointed out that the ability to regulate the "internal environment" gave tissues and organs of higher organisms a degree of independence from the organism's external environment. Such regulation, which tends to counteract external altering influences, has been called "homeostasis" (for classical paper, see Cannon, 1929). At the cellular level, homeostasis must, of necessity, involve the interaction between a cell and its immediate environment, the extracellular matrix.

Whereas the milieu interieur of mature organisms is regulated by mechanisms that function to maintain a degree of constancy, the embryonic milieu interieur is a dynamic one, undergoing relatively rapid qualitative and quantitative changes as ontogenesis proceeds. Thus the immediate environment of cells in different regions of the embryo changes as the extracellular matrix undergoes changes. Much as in the adult, the physical and chemical characteristics of the extracellular matrix in the embryo dictate the properties of the embryonic cellular environments.

2. Embryonic Considerations

Many of the substances found in the extracellular matrix are cell products. These extracellular products may change with development, thus permitting one to speak of the *differentiation* of extracellular matrices in terms of their molecular composition. However, differentiative changes in the extracellular matrix may occur concomitantly with differentiation of cells themselves, and in some cases (especially in connective tissue development) the level of differentiation of a particular cell type is defined by the matrix it produces (e.g., the chondrocyte). The near concomitance of cytodifferentiation and matrix differentiation (or at least, detectable *changes* in matrix composition) raise interesting problems. Do changes in extracellular matrices mediate cytodifferentiation by limiting or expanding the cell's choices of expression? If so, is this a passive effect, for example, restricting the diffusion of a particular substance, or is it active, perhaps a direct interaction of matrix with hypothetical cell surface receptors? Thus, extracellular matrices are of interest from at least three standpoints: their development and differentiation may reflect the acquisition of mature (i.e., differentiated) functions of the cells that produce them and, in turn, may influence the phenotypic expression of the differentiated state. Matrix may also play a role, direct or indirect, in events of tissue and organ morphogenesis.

Implicit in models of cell–matrix interaction is the assumption that the properties and composition of the normal extracellular matrix can be determined and that such determinations can be correlated spatially and temporally with normal developmental events. This chapter does not review earlier work on specific embryonic functions of matrix (for some recent examples, see Bernfield and Banerjee, 1972; Bernfield *et al.*, 1972, 1973; Bernfield and Wessells, 1970; Grobstein, 1967; Hay, 1973; Toole, 1973; Zwaan and Hendrix, 1973; see also discussion in Hay and Dodson, 1973). Rather it attempts to define the levels at which some embryonic matrices have been examined and explore the restrictions imposed by these levels upon an understanding of matrix function.

Since matrix is a complex, dynamic, integrated entity, alteration in concentration levels of single components may result in profound changes in the matrix as an entity. As such, an ontogenic effect of any substituent may be the result of its integration into the entire matrix, rather than a direct individual effect. Integration of a number of different components may generate information unique to the integrated system. Thus, the enticing experimental approach of adding or deleting one or more matrix macromolecules from cells cultured in artificial medium may elicit responses that have no *in vivo* counterpart. These problems could be circumvented if cells could be grown *in vitro* in an artificial matrix that is compositionally identical to its *in situ* counterpart, and the deletion and replacement of one or more substituents done in a controlled manner. Such an approach does not require the assumption that individual matrix components normally have separable, discretely definable functions or have specific targets. Instead, it considers matrix as an integrated complex entity to which cells respond; it does not attempt to discern artificial properties of unusual concentrations of any single substituent.

Information about embryonic extracellular matrix is at present inadequate for comprehensive descriptions of matrix components for any developing system. Since experimental manipulation of poorly characterized material is difficult, I shall, in succeeding sections, be concerned principally with descriptive biochemistry of the development of some embryonic matrices, morphological correlates, and methods of investigation.

II. Macromolecular Composition of Extracellular Matrix

A. COLLAGEN

In its various genetic types, collagen is the most common protein found in higher vertebrates. The collagen molecule, tropocollagen, consists of three subunits called α chains. Based on a variety of criteria, at least five types of α chains can be identified, four known varieties of α1 chains and only one variety of α2. The different α1 chains are designated α1(I), α1(II), 1(III), and 1(IV) (Miller and Matukas, 1969; Miller *et al.*, 1971; Chung and Miller, 1974; Kefalides, 1972). Known combinations of α1 and α2 chains result in the following types of collagen: Type I chain composition: $[\alpha 1(I)]_2$ α2 (Piez *et al.*, 1963; Nold *et al.*, 1970); Type II chain composition: $[\alpha 1(II)]_3$ (Trelstad *et al.*, 1970); Type III chain composition: $[\alpha 1(III)]_3$ (Miller *et al.*, 1971; Chung and Miller, 1974); and Type IV chain composition: $[\alpha 1(IV)]_3$ (Kefalides, 1971). Many of these types of collagen have dissimilar distributions within the mature vertebrate body and may make their appearance at different times in ontogenesis.

1. Alpha Chains

The subunits of tropocollagen, called α chains, have a molecular weight of 95,000 or 115,000. Most α chains contain approximately 1040 amino acids. Glycine represents about 33%, proline and its hydroxylated derivatives about 20%, and alanine about 15%; the balance represents more common amino acids (see Grant and Prockop, 1972). Certain amino acid residues are altered by posttranslational modifications. For example, some lysine and proline residues are hydroxylated (proline to 3- and 4-hydroxyproline). Aldehydes of lysine and hydroxylysine are formed as well as mono- or disaccharide glucose and galactose hydroxylysine derivatives (see Traub and Piez, 1971; Gallop et al., 1972).

One can recognize different α chains on the basis of a number of compositional criteria. Chains differ in amino acid composition (Table I), posttranslational modifications (see Table II), and amino acid sequence as indicated by analysis of cyanogen bromide peptides. These peptides are fragments of the original α chain resulting from cleavage at methionine residues. Because of differences in number and location of methionine residues, each α chain has characteristic CNBr peptides (see Fig. 1).

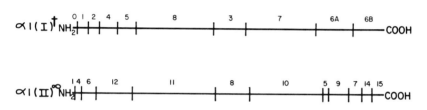

α I (III)† Only CB3 and CB4,5 peptides identified, other peptides may be very homologous to α I(I) peptides.

α I (IV)° 12 CNBr peptides, order unknown.

FIG. 1. The linear order of α-chain CNBr peptides. Relative lengths are directly proportional to the relative sizes of different peptides. Key to references: † Piez et al. (1969) [note that chick α1(I) chains lack the methionine residue between 6A and 6B, having one less peptide]; ∞ Miller et al. (1973); ° Kefalides (1972); + Miller et al. (1971), Volpin and Veis (1971, 1973); * Vuust et al. (1970); Igarashi et al. (1970).

α1(III) has been distinguished from α1(I) by differences in the two cyanogen bromide peptides called α1CB3 and α1CB4,5 (Miller et al., 1971; Volpin and Veis, 1971, 1973). The same two peptides can be used to distinguish α1(I) from α1(II) chains. (see Table III; Fig. 1). Attention is drawn to the α1(IV) chain, which is larger than other α chains

TABLE I

AMINO ACID COMPOSITION AND SIZE OF α CHAINS[a]

Residue[b]	α1(I),[c] MW 95,000	α1(II),[d] MW 95,000	α1(III),[e] MW 95,000	α1(IV),[f] MW 115,000	α2,[g] MW 95,000
HyL	5.2	24	5	58.5	10.4
Lys	30	13	30	15	22
His	2	2	6	10	8
Arg	50	51	46	19	52
HyP³	0.9	2	—	9.5	1
HyP	107	106	125	132	100
Asp	42	43	42	50	52
Thr	19	27	13	22	21
Ser	27	27	39	42	32
Glu	77	89	71	78	69
Pro	120	118	107	68	121
Gly	328	336	350	348	339
Ala	129	106	96	39	108
Val	14	16	14	29	29
½ Cys	—	—	2	4	—
Ile	6	7.2	13	29	18
Leu	20	27	22	54	33
Tyr	2	2	3	3	2
Phe	12	15	8	26	14
Met	8	12	8	11	5

[a] Values are expressed as residues per molecule. There are species differences in collagen types, but these are minor and do not obscure the compositional difference of collagen α-chain types. Note that chick α1(I) chains have one less methionine residue than rat, bovine, or human α1(I) chains. Noninteger values for HyL and HyP are given, as some slight variability in hydroxylation of lysines and proline residues does exist.

[b] Standard abbreviations are used for normally occurring amino acid residues. Specific abbreviations unique to collagen are: HyL for hydroxylysine, HyP for 4-hydroxyproline, and HyP³ for 3-hydroxyproline.

[c] Chick skin collagen (Kang et al. 1969b).

[d] Chick sternal cartilage (Miller, 1971a,b,c).

[e] Human aorta collagen (Chung and Miller, 1974).

[f] Bovine lens capsule (Kefalides, 1972).

[g] Chick skin collagen (Kang et al., 1969a,b).

(Table I) and differs markedly in amino acid composition (Table I) and posttranslational modifications (Table II).

2. The Tropocollagen Molecule

Type I tropocollagen contains two α1(I) chains and one α2 chain (Piez et al., 1963; Nold et al., 1970). All other collagens contain three

TABLE II

POSTTRANSLATIONAL MODIFICATIONS OF α CHAINS

Modification[a]	α1(I)[b]	α1(II)[c]	α1(III)[d]	α1(IV)[e]	α2[f]
HyP + HyP³/total Pro	108/228	108/220	125/232	142/210	101/222
HyP/α chain	107	106	125	132	100
HyP³/α chain	0.9	2	0	9.5	1
HyL/total HyL	5/35	24/37	5/35	59/74	11/32
Percent covalently bound hexose	0.5	5.5	—	10–12%	0.5

[a] Abbreviations unique to collagen: HyP, hydroxyproline; HyP³, 3-hydroxyproline; HyL, hydroxylysine.
[b] Kang et al. (1969b).
[c] Miller (1971a,b,c).
[d] Chung and Miller (1974).
[e] Kefalides (1971).
[f] Kang et al. (1969a).

α1 chains (Trelstad et al., 1970; Kefalides, 1971; Miller et al., 1971; Chung and Miller, 1974). These different types of collagen have somewhat tissue-specific distributions (Table IV). The crossbanded collagen fibril seen with the electron microscope represents a polarized, linear assembly of tropocollagen molecules that are regularly quarter-staggered (Hodge, 1967).

The α chains are held together in a characteristic helical array in the tropocollagen molecule by noncovalent forces (Burge and Hynes, 1959; von Hippel and Harrington, 1960; Altgelt et al., 1961). Small portions of the amino and carboxy termini are not part of the helix. These regions have sometimes been called nonhelical regions, or telopeptides. Common acidic and basic amino acids are concentrated in these terminal segments (see Gallop et al., 1972).

Tropocollagen structure is independent of covalent bonds between α chains. In the absence of covalent bonds, tropocollagen can be thermally denatured into component α chains, known historically as gelatin (Bailey, 1968). Denatured α chains are sensitive to proteolytic enzymes, such as trypsin, pepsin, papain, and chymotrypsin. However, in their native tropocollagen state only the nonhelical segments are sensitive to these enzymes (Bornstein et al., 1966).

Collagen extractable by mild procedures (3% acetic acid) contains few covalently linked α chains (e.g., tendon collagen) whereas the highly insoluble collagen of bone has α chains that are extensively cross-linked (Piez et al., 1963; Miller et al., 1967). These covalent interchain cross-

TABLE III

COMPOSITION OF TWO α1 CHAIN CYANOGEN BROMIDE PEPTIDE HOMOLOGS
FOR α1(I), α1(II), AND α1(III) CHAINS[a,b]

	α1CB3			α1CB4,5[c]		
Residue	α1(I)	α1(II)	α1(III)	α1(I)	α1(II)	α1(III)
Hyl	0.2	2.5	0.3	1.3	2.9	0.2
Lys	4.8	4.2	7.0	3.7	2.9	1.6
His	0	0	0	1	1	1
Arg	6	7	4	5	4	5
Hyp	15	16	19	9	11	12
Asp	6	4	8	6	4	4
Thr	0	3	4	1	1	1
Ser	3	3	1	2	3	4
Glu	15	14	12	6	6	6
Pro	15	17	19	8	7	7
Gly	49	49	49	28	28	28
Ala	21	14	15	7	6	9
Val	4	2	1	0	2	1
Ile	0	0	0	0	0	1
Leu	3	6	5	3	2	1
Tyr	0	0	0	0	1	0
Phe	3	3	1	1	1	1
Met	1	1	1	2	1	1
Total residues	146	146	146	84	84	84

[a] Values are expressed as residues per peptide.

[b] From Miller et al. (1971); peptide isolated from human skin and cartilage. This analysis has been borne out by the homology of the amino acid sequences of these CNBr peptides (Butler et al., 1974).

[c] Note that for α1(I) there are 2 peptides, CB4 and CB5, but there is only one peptide for α(II) and α1(III) chains, referred to as CB4,5, indicating that it contains both CB4 and CB5, as originally identified for α1(I) collagen. Subsequently, Miller (1971a,b,c) devised a new α1(II) peptide nomenclature, for which α1(II)CB3 becomes α1(II)CB8 and α1(II)CB4,5 becomes α1(II)CB12.

links involve predominantly lysine and hydroxylysine residues and their aldehyde derivative (see Tanzer, 1973). If enzymatic formation of aldehyde derivatives is prevented (for example, by β-aminopropionitrile) (Narayanan et al., 1972), or the reactivity of formed aldehydes is blocked (for example, by D-penicillamine) (Nimni, 1965), cross-links do not occur and collagen is rendered extractable by mild procedures, such as use of 1 M NaCl. Collagen synthesized after addition of these agents (called lathyrogens) can therefore be quantitatively recovered and readily analyzed (Tanzer, 1965; Golub et al., 1968; Glimcher et al., 1969). There is increasing evidence that collagen may be normally associ-

TABLE IV

CHAIN COMPOSITION AND MATURE TISSUE DISTRIBUTION
OF DIFFERENT COLLAGEN TYPES

Collagen	Chain composition	Sources, mature tissues
Type I	$[\alpha 1(I)]_2\alpha 2$	Skin, bone, tendon
Type II	$[\alpha 1(II)]_3$	Cartilage
Type III	$[\alpha 1(III)]_3$	Skin, dentine, aorta
Type IV	$[\alpha 1(IV)]_3$	Some basal laminae such as lens capsule, Descemet's membrane, renal glomerular and alveolar

ated with noncollagenous protein by means of covalent bonds that are also sensitive to these agents (Veis and Perry, 1967; Volpin and Veis, 1973).

B. ANIONIC POLYSACCHARIDES (GLYCOSAMINOGLYCANS)

Anionic polysaccharides are common constituents of all extracellular matrices, although precise composition varies according to location and age. Those examined most often are the carbohydrate portions of glycosaminoglycans. Glycosaminoglycans are large molecules containing linear polymers of monosaccharides (ranging from $n = 10$ for keratan sulfate to $n = 2500$ for hyaluronate) that, with the possible exception of hyaluronate, are covalently linked to polypeptides. Thus, each molecule contains a proteinaceous core to which are attached carbohydrate chains. The protein is generally the minor component, 10–20% w/w (see Schubert and Hamerman, 1968).

Each glycosaminoglycan polysaccharide has a characteristic chain length—hence molecular weight. Keratan sulfates are smallest, ranging from about MW 3000 to 6000; chondroitin sulfates range around MW 3×10^4 to 4×10^4 (Tanford et al., 1964), and hyaluronate ranges from MW 1×10^6 to 1×10^7 (Balazs, 1958). Polysaccharide chains of different glycosaminoglycans show differences in their monomeric subunit composition (Table V) as well as size differences. In general, N-acetylhexosamine is linked (β, 1–4) to a uronic acid which, in turn, is linked (β, 1–6) to N-acetylhexosamine, and this sequence is repeated. In the case of keratan sulfate, D-galactose substitutes for the uronic acid.

With the clear exception of hyaluronate, matrix glycosaminoglycans are sulfated. Chondroitin sulfates are sulfated on either the 4 or the 6

TABLE V

Polysaccharide	Hexosamine	Hexuronate	Linkages
Hyaluronate (HA)	N-Ac[a]-glucosamine	Glucuronate	β, 1–3, 1–4
Chondroitin (Ch)[b]	N-Ac-galactosamine	Glucuronate	β, 1–3, 1–4
Chondroitin sulfate (ChS) 4,6[b]	N-Ac-galactosamine (sulfated)	Glucuronate	β, 1–3, 1–4
Heparan sulfate (HS)[c]	N-Ac-glucosamine (sulfated)	Glucuronate Iduronate	β, 1–4 β, 1–4
Heparin (H)[c]	N-Ac-glucosamine (sulfated)	Glucuronate Iduronate	β, 1–4 β, 1–4
Keratan sulfate (KS)[d]	N-Ac-glucosamine (sulfated) galactose	—	β, 1–3, 1–4
Dermatan sulfate (DS) (ChS B)[e]	N-Ac-galactosamine (sulfated)	Iduronate	β, 1–3, 1–4

[a] N-Ac = N-acetyl.
[b] Rodén (1970).
[c] Lindahl (1970); Cifonelli (1970).
[d] Greiling et al. (1970).
[e] Fransson (1970).

carbon (chondroitin 4-sulfate and 6-sulfate, respectively) whereas the hexosamine amine nitrogens of heparan sulfate and heparin are sulfated. In keratan sulfate, the sulfate is covalently linked to the sixth carbon of the N-acetyl-D-glucosamine residue. Chondroitin, which is another unsulfated glycosaminoglycan, may not exist as part of the extracellular matrix, but may be exclusively intracellular (see Rodén, 1970; Fransson, 1970; Greiling et al., 1970; Lindahl, 1970; Cifonelli, 1970).

Glycosaminoglycan polysaccharides are polyanions. Normally they exist in conjunction with counterions, generally Na^+; hence they are salts, such as sodium hyaluronate (see Schubert and Hamerman, 1968).

With the possible exception of hyaluronate, matrix polysaccharides are associated with protein. Chondroitin sulfate, for example, exists in the extracellular space, not as a simple polymer of sugar but linked to protein. This complex is called proteochondroitin sulfate. Most demonstrations of matrix glycosamingolycans in situ involve histochemical reaction with the sugar polymer, and, as we shall see in more detail, biochemical identification is also principally based upon properties of, or reactions involving, the carbohydrate moiety; relatively little is known about the protein moiety.

Although the partial characterization of the protein core of the cartilage proteochondroitin sulfate has been made (Pal et al., 1966; Franek and Dunstone, 1967; Rosenberg and Schubert, 1967; Sadjera and Hascall, 1969; Hascall and Sadjera, 1970; Rosenberg *et al.*, 1970), virtually nothing is known about the protein core in nonchondrogenic tissues or in developing systems. Does it change during development? Is it tissue specific? It is unfortunate that the protein moiety of glycosaminoglycans has been largely ignored since it represents the only portion of these molecules that comprises directly translated gene products.

In cartilage, about 8–10% (w/w) of proteochondroitin sulfate consists of a series of small (MW 15,000) proteins containing high levels of proline, glutamic acid, glycine, serine, and aspartic acid. Although there may be significant variation between core protein isolated from different cartilages, it is not known whether developmental differences occur.

The protein core is extremely important in chondroitin sulfate biosynthesis. It is synthesized, presumably on membrane-bound polysomes, before synthesis of the polysaccharide begins. Xylose is linked to serine and followed by the sequential addition of two galactose and a glucuronate residue. Thereafter, sequential addition of N-acetylgalactosamine and D-glucuronate subunits continues, up to about 60 repeat units (Thorp and Dorfman, 1963; Telser *et al.*, 1965; Horwitz and Dorfman, 1968).

It is interesting to consider protein-polysaccharides in terms of potential information contained within the molecule. Clearly an $n = 150$ polymer of roughly 20 different independently sorted components (the protein core) can code vastly more information than an $n = 60$ polymer of two different alternating components (polysaccharide chain), especially in words of a small number of letters. Hence, the protein core may be developmentally more significant than the large carbohydrate component. A complete understanding of putative functions of glycosaminoglycans during development cannot be deduced until the characteristics of the protein core are known.

C. GLYCOPROTEINS

Glycoproteins are molecules containing polysaccharide covalently linked to protein but, unlike glycosaminoglycans, they are principally protein (see Table VI). The polysaccharide component is relatively small and is linked covalently to protein by serine, threonine, or asparagine residues. The polysaccharides of glycoproteins are more heterogeneous than of the glycosaminoglycans. They contain additionally L-fucose, D-mannose, D-arabinose, neuraminic acid, N-acetylneuraminic acid linked by glycosidic linkages not found in glycosaminoglycans. In short, whereas glycosaminoglycans are highly regular polysaccharides linked to a minor protein component, glycoproteins are principally protein linked to a minor, more diverse carbohydrate moiety. Some molecules, such as

TABLE VI

COMPOSITION AND SIZE OF GLYCOPROTEINS

Glycoprotein	Size of polysac-charides[a,b]	Types of monosaccharides[b]	Glycosidic linkages	Size of poly-peptide
Ovalbumin, hen	1560	Mannose, N-acetyl-glucosamine	α, 2–6	45,000[c]
Ribonuclease B, bovine	1600	Mannose, N-acetyl-glucosamine	α, 2–6	13,700[c]
Thyroglobulin, calf	11250	Mannose, N-acetyl glucosamine	α, 2–6	669,000[c]
Transferrin, human	6200	Mannose, N-acetyl-glucosamine, galactose, sialic acid	α, 2–6	90,000[d]
Fibrinogen, bovine	4200	Mannose, N-acetyl-glucosamine, galactose, sialic acid	α, 2–6	341,000[d]
IgG, human	4600	Mannose, N-acetyl-glucosamine, galactose, fucose, sialic acid	α, 2–6	150,000[c]

[a] Note that none of the polysaccharide chains are longer than 10–12 monosaccharides and that a particular polypeptide may have one or a number of similar polysaccharide chains.
[b] Sharon (1966).
[c] Klotz and Darnall (1969).
[d] White et al. (1964).

keratan sulfate, fall somewhere between these extremes and may be categorized in either class (see Spiro, 1970a).

A great variety of biological macromolecules are glycoproteins. Those best characterized (e.g., serum glycoproteins, thyroglogulin, ribonuclease B) are not permanent structural components of the extracellular matrix. Noncollagenous glycoproteins of the extracellular matrix, such as those of bone and cartilage and those associated with cell coats, although most germane to our discussion, are most poorly characterized. For a discussion of glycoprotein biosynthesis, see Spiro (1970b).

III. Methods of Analyzing Extracellular Matrix Macromolecules

Analysis of matrix macromolecules can be divided into two general categories: analysis of total composition (bulk analysis) and analysis of macromolecules synthesized at a particular time (synthetic analysis). Each approach provides different types of information, has its own inherent limitations, and may provide seemingly contradictory data.

Bulk analysis defines total molecular composition and does not distinguish when any given molecular species were made. Bulk analyses require relatively large amounts of material and may be relatively insensitive for identification of minor components.

Synthetic analysis provides little information regarding total composition, but rather measures newly synthesized molecules. If different components are degraded at different rates, the synthetic profile may differ vastly from actual composition. Thus, synthetic analyses may overemphasize changes in composition or may reflect spurious changes. However, synthetic analyses, especially those using radioactive label, generally require much less material, making this a valuable and useful approach if turnover levels are low.

Historically, the macromolecular composition of extracellular matrices have been determined by the analysis of the total composition of mature connective tissue extracellular matrices. Analyses of embryonic extracellular matrices generally have identified only newly synthesized macromolecules (synthetic analysis) and interpreted them as though they represented the total composition. In order to understand the nature of embryonic matrices, it is necessary to appreciate the relative advantages and shortcomings of both bulk and synthetic analyses.

A. TOTAL COMPOSITIONAL (BULK) ANALYSIS

The methods of determining the total composition of collagen and glycosaminoglycan polysaccharides will be presented separately. The subsequent discussion of synthetic analysis of extracellular matrix macromolecules will draw heavily on the techniques and interpretations used for bulk analysis.

1. Total Compositional (Bulk) Analysis of Collagen

The absolute or relative amount of collagen can be established by measuring colorimetrically the level of hydroxyproline after reaction with ninhydrin after hydrolysis and separation from proline (Stegemann, 1958). Although the aromatic amino acid (e.g., phenylalanine, tyrosine, and tryptophan) composition of most proteins allows their detection by measuring optical density (OD) at 280 nm, collagen contains very low levels of these amino acids (see Table I). Solutions of collagen are, therefore, assayed by measuring OD 230 nm; at this wavelength, unfortunately, other compounds absorb equally well. Obviously, neither of these procedures can distinguish different types of collagen. Procedures that enable such distinctions to be made will be discussed next and are summarized in Table VII.

TABLE VII

ANALYSIS OF COLLAGEN

Procedure	Identifies
Sodium dodecyl sulfate–acrylamide gel electrophoresis and molecular sieve chromatography in denaturing solvents	γ- and β-Procollagen and α chains as well as $\alpha 1(IV)$ chains
CM-cellulose chromatography of α chains	$\alpha 1$, $\alpha 2$, $\alpha 1(IV)$, $\beta 1,1$, and $\beta 1,2$ chains
DEAE-cellulose of isolated $\alpha 1$ chains	$\alpha 1(II)$ chains or $\alpha 1$ chains with the same level of hydroxylysine as $\alpha 1(II)$ chains
Amino acid composition	$\alpha 1(I)$, $\alpha 1(II)$, $\alpha 1(IV)$, and $\alpha 2$ chains
Analysis of cyanogen bromide peptides of isolated α chains	$\alpha 1(I)$, $\alpha 1(II)$, $\alpha 1(III)$, $\alpha 1(IV)$, and $\alpha 2$ chains, and can show any covalently linked noncollagenous peptides

a. Extraction and Purification of Collagen. The method used to extract collagen depends dramatically on the tissue extracted (Table VIII). Highly insoluble collagens can also be extracted by digestion with cyanogen bromide in 70% formic acid, which will release most of the collagen as CNBr peptides (Miller *et al.*, 1971; Volpin and Veis, 1971, 1973). Recently, pepsin digestion of nonmineralized connective tissues has been employed to study their insoluble collagens (Miller, 1971c; Chung and Miller, 1974).

TABLE VIII

COLLAGEN EXTRACTABILITY

Solvent	Tendon	Skin	Bone	Cartilage
3% Acetic acid	100%	50–70%	2–5%	0%
LiCl, $MgCl_2$, $CaCl_2$, or guanidine HCl	100%	90%	80–90%	5–10%
Pepsin or papain digestion, followed by LiCl, $MgCl_2$, $CaCl_2$, or guanidine-HCl extraction	100%	100%	80–90%	90–100%

The problem of analysis of the insoluble bone, skin, and cartilage collagens has been circumvented by the use of lathyrogens, such as β-aminopropionitrile or D-penicillamine, which should render salt-soluble collagen synthesized in their presence (Martin *et al.*, 1963; Miller *et al.*, 1967; Golub *et al.*, 1968; Glimcher *et al.*, 1969). As such, this approach actually examines synthesis rather than total composition. Most often, in the study of embryonic collagen, these lathyrogens have been introduced into chick embryos late in development. This has precluded ready extraction and analysis of collagen synthesized earlier in development and as a consequence has led to the failure to appreciate changes in the collagens of bone, skin, and cartilage during earlier embryonic development.

The unique type of collagen, $[\alpha1(IV)]_3$, found in some basal laminae is, under some conditions, particularly difficult to extract (see Kefalides, 1973). However, in some *in vitro* conditions as well as in very early embryos, this collagen is readily extractable in neutral salt solutions. Extractability of collagens depends, to some extent, on extracellular interactions between collagen molecules as well as between collagen and other extracellular molecules. This makes it extremely difficult, if not impossible, to accurately predict the extractability of collagen molecules in early embryos by extrapolating from known extractabilities in older or mature tissue.

The unique amino acid composition of collagen allows for its selective precipitation by addition of high salt ($2\ M$ NaCl) acidification or removal of salt (Gross, 1958; Glimcher *et al.*, 1964). However, these precipitations are not quantitative and tend (at least in this laboratory) to selectively lose type I collagen relative to other types. Collagen can be purified from glycosaminoglycans by precipitation of the latter in 1% cetyl pyridinium chloride (Miller and Matukas, 1969) or by step elution from DEAE-cellulose (Miller, 1971a). Collagen can also be purified by molecular sieve chromatography on the basis of its unique size, or by ion-exchange chromatography on carboxymethyl cellulose on the basis of its charge:mass ratio (Piez *et al.*, 1960, 1963).

b. Fractionation and Characterization of Collagen Types. Collagen is generally characterized on the basis of types of α chains present after thermal denaturation of tropocollagen. Cross-linked collagen extracted by strong denaturing solvents or pepsin digestion may contain, in addition to α chains, significant quantities of β and γ components, which may significantly muddle subsequent analyses.

i. Fractionation according to size. Size determination is necessary to ensure the presence of only α chains and the absence of noncollagenous protein or aggregates of α chains (β and γ components) of smaller molecular weight. The presence of the slightly larger $\alpha1(IV)$ chains can also be detected. The size of collagen chains can be evaluated by chromatography on a molecular sieve column of appropriate pore size (e.g., Bio-Gel P-150, P-300, A-1.5) in a suitable denaturing solvent [0.1% sodium dodecyl sulfate (SDS), $2\ M$ LiCl, $1\ M$ CaCl$_2$, or $6\ M$ guanidine-HCl], calibrated by the elution position of polypeptides of known molecular weights (Fish et al., 1969). Alternatively, the size of collagen chains can be determined by electrophoresis on acrylamide gels in 0.1% SDS (Weber and Osborn, 1969). However, collagen binds SDS differently from most proteins (Furthmayr and Timpl, 1971), making it impossible to use the relative migration of noncollagen proteins to calibrate the gels. To calibrate the relative electrophoretic migration against molecular weight, it is necessary to use as standards collagen, α, β procollagen chains, and α-chain CNBr peptides whose molecular weight has been measured by molecular sieve chromatography.

Collagen $\alpha 1$ and $\alpha 2$ chains can be separated by SDS–acrylamide gel electrophoresis (providing that the gel pore size is sufficiently small) by using gels with acrylamide concentrations of 5.5% or higher. This separation results probably from subtle differences in SDS binding, *not* from differences in molecular weight. Finally, cyanogen bromide peptides from $1(I)$, $\alpha 1(II)$, $\alpha 1(IV)$, and $\alpha 2$ chains can be distinguished by their electrophoresis on SDS–acrylamide gels made with 7.5% acrylamide. However, it is difficult to analyze the peptides of more than one type of α chain simultaneously because of the large number of different bands. Collagen chains can also be separated into α, β, and γ components by electrophoresis (Nagai et al., 1964; François and Glimcher, 1965, 1967).

ii. *Fractionation of collagen α chains on CM-cellulose.* Thermally denatured collagen, with or without previous purification, can be fractionated into component α chains by chromatography on CM-cellulose at pH 4.8 and 42°C by elution with a linear 0 to 0.1 M NaCl salt gradient (Piez et al., 1960, 1963; Miller, 1971a). Noncollagenous proteins elute first, followed by $\alpha 1$ and then $\alpha 2$ chains. If the collagen is cross-linked, $\beta 1,1$ components (two $\alpha 1$ chains) may be seen eluting just after $\alpha 1$ chains, and $\beta 1,2$ components (one $\alpha 1$ and one $\alpha 2$ chain) elute just before $\alpha 2$ chains. It is possible to separate $\alpha 1(IV)$ chains from other $\alpha 1$ chains and partially separate $\alpha 1(II)$ from $\alpha 1(I)$ chains by use of an extended salt gradient elution (Miller and Matukas, 1969; Kefalides, 1971; Johnson et al., 1974). Finally, subtle variations between $\alpha 1$ chains, such as different aldehyde content (Piez et al., 1966) or those resulting from proteolytic digestion of nonhelical regions (Bornstein et al., 1966) can produce an $\alpha 1$ peak that chromatographs markedly heterogeneously. This suggests strongly that elution differences shown by CM-cellulose chromatography require independent confirmation to exclude such trivial explanations.

For non-cross-linked collagen, the ratio of $\alpha 1$ chains to $\alpha 2$ chains can be used to estimate the percentage of Type I collagen relative to $(\alpha 1)_3$ collagens (Fig. 2). For example, 2 $\alpha 1$ chains per $\alpha 2$ chain indicates 100% Type I, 5 $\alpha 1$ chains per $\alpha 2$ chain indicates 50% Type I, and 20 $\alpha 1$ chains

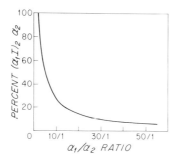

Fig. 2. A graphical representation of the interpretation of the percent composition of Type I collagen by the ratio of α1 to α2 chains. This interpretation is based on presence of 2 α1 chains per α2 chains and the absence of α2 chains in all other known types of collagen see Table IV). The relative amount of (α1)₃ collagen is simply the reciprocal of the value for Type I collagen.

per α2 chain indicates 25% Type I collagen. The absence of α2 chains suggests the absence of Type I collagen. Finally, the yields obtained by CM-cellulose chromatography can depend dramatically on both the nature of collagen assayed as well as the chromatographic procedure. For example, nonlathyritic collagen chromatographed in the absence of urea can have a 35–50% yield (Piez *et al.*, 1963) whereas lathyritic collagen chromatographed in the presence of 1.3 M urea may be recovered with a 95–99% yield. If CM-cellulose chromatography of collagen α chains is employed to determine the type of collagen present, and especially if attempts are made to quantitate the presence of different collagen types, it is of utmost importance to obtain high yields.

iii. *Fractionation of α1 chains on DEAE-cellulose.* The elution of α chains from CM-cellulose can determine the relative amount of Type I collagen and Type IV collagen but provide no direct evidence for distinguishing between Type II and Type III collagen. Stepwise elution of α1 chains from DEAE-cellulose (Trelstad *et al.*, 1972) allows separation of α1 chains into two fractions: α1(I) plus α1(III) chains eluting at pH 8.3 and α1(II) chains eluting at pH 7.5. Preliminary evidence in this laboratory indicates α1(IV) chains elute at a much lower pH. Thus, separation of α1 chains by means of DEAE-cellulose is particularly valuable in determining whether there is [α1(II)]₃ collagen present when the α1 to α2 chain ratios, as determined by CM-cellulose, exceed 2:1. Generally, α1 chains are first separated from β and α2 chains by means of CM-cellulose chromatography. This prevents the pH 8.3 elution of α1(I) and α1(III) chains from being obscured by these components.

However, there are indications that DEAE-cellulose chromatography separates collagen $\alpha 1$ chains on the basis of differences in posttranslational modifications (e.g., lysine hydroxylation and/or glycosylation) rather than by differences in amino acid composition or sequence. For example, normal $\alpha 1$(I) chains which have about one-tenth the hydroxylysine and one-tenth the covalently bonded hexose of normal $\alpha 1$(II) chains (see Table II) do not coelute with $\alpha 1$(II) chains. However, $\alpha 1$(I) chains of experimentally rachitic bone have an abnormally high level of hydroxylysine (Toole et al., 1972; Barnes et al., 1973) and hence coelute with $\alpha 1$(II) chains (Trelstad et al., 1972). As a corollary, it is predictable that an $\alpha 1$(II) chain with an abnormally low hydroxylysine content would coelute with normal $\alpha 1$(I).

iv. *Analysis of amino acid composition.* Although different types of α chains do have distinctive amino acid compositions, the relatively small percentage of difference (ca. 5–10%) between different α chains (see Table I) makes distinguishing between them by amino acid compositions alone very difficult and unreliable. The amino acid composition of purified $\alpha 1$(I) chain, for example, can be compared to that expected for $\alpha 1$(I) chains. An $\alpha 1$ chain fraction with an amino acid composition partially similar to both $\alpha 1$(I) and $\alpha 1$(II) chains could either represent a mixture of $\alpha 1$(I) and $\alpha 1$(II) chains or a new type of $\alpha 1$ chain. As some of the compositional differences between α chains represent posttranslational events, they cannot reliably be used to distinguish definitely between different genetic types of collagen. Such ambiguity could be resolved only by analyzing the amino acid sequence by means of CNBr peptides. Hence determination of amino acid composition may not be an especially useful analytic tool for the routine characterization of different types of collagen.

v. *Analysis of α chain cyanogen bromide peptides.* The types of collagen α chains present can be determined by either analyzing all different peptides or by analyzing selectively for certain diagnostic peptides that distinguish the different kinds of α chains. If one analyzes all released peptides, a series of different analyses must be performed (for examples, see Kang et al., 1969a,b; Piez et al., 1969; Click and Bornstein, 1970; Miller, 1971b,c; Kefalides, 1972; Volpin and Veis, 1973). Alternatively, one can fractionate in a single step all the CNBr peptides on CM-cellulose at pH 3.6 and identify the presence of certain diagnostic peptides (Miller et al., 1971, 1973). Collagen $\alpha 1$(I), $\alpha 1$(II), and $\alpha 1$(III) chains contain two pairs of homologous CNBr peptides (see Section II, A). Chromatography on CM cellulose at pH 3.6 with a linear 0.015 to 0.15 M NaCl salt gradient allows separation of all three peptides of both homologs (Miller et al., 1971). Peptides from $\alpha 1$(IV) chains chromatograph very differently from other $\alpha 1$ chain peptides, and the discrepancy is readily apparent (Kefalides, 1972). Finally, $\alpha 2$ chain peptides elute much later in the chromatograph, and their presence is also readily apparent (Kang et al., 1969b). Thus, it is possible to determine the presence of all five known types of α chains in a mixture by a single chromatographic step which distinguishes between different genetic types of α chains on the basis of their different amino acid sequences.

2. Total Compositional Analysis of Glycosaminoglycan Polysaccharide

Glycosaminoglycan polysaccharides are analyzed by differences in charge:mass ratio, differential sensitivity to specific enzymes or hydrolytic conditions, and the identification of specific disaccharides and monosaccharides after hydrolysis. The relative or absolute amount of glycosaminoglycan polysaccharide in a tissue or extract can be estimated using the carbazole reaction for hexuronate (Dische, 1947). The relative quantities of glycosaminoglycan in different solutions can be estimated by measuring the absorbance of the solution, although this measurement is best applied to solutions of glycosaminoglycan which are at least partially pure (see Section III, A, 1).

a. *Extraction and Purification.* Glycosaminoglycan polysaccharides are generally liberated by dissolution of tissue proteins with Pronase or papain. Alternatively, protein-polysaccharides can be extracted in strong denaturing solvents (e.g., LiCl, $CaCl_2$, $MgCl_2$, or guanidine HCl) (Sadjera and Hascall, 1969; Hascall and Sadjera, 1970; Rosenberg et al., 1970), and the protein moeity can be removed proteolytically or by periodate cleavage of the protein-polysaccharide linkage. Glycosaminoglycan polysaccharide can be purified from other components by precipitation with ethanol, potassium acetate, cetyl pyridinium chloride (CPC), or cetyl pyridinium bromide.

b. *Fractionation of Glycosaminoglycan Polysaccharide.* Different glycosaminoglycan polysaccharides can be separated by salt elution from DEAE-cellulose (Silbert and Deluca, 1969) or by solubilization of CPC precipitates by steps of increasing salt concentration (Antonopoulos et al., 1964). Different glycosaminoglycan polysaccharides can also be fractionated by molecular sieve chromatography in accordance with their characteristic differences in molecular weight.

c. *Analysis of Types of Glycosaminoglycan Polysaccharides.* The chromatographic behavior on DEAE-cellulose (Silbert and Deluca, 1969), electrophoretic behavior on cellulose acetate strips (for example, see Wessler, 1970; Manasek et al., 1973), or determining the ionic strength necessary to dissolve a CPC-precipitated glycosaminoglycan polysaccharide (Antonopoulos et al., 1964) can be used to distinguish between different polysaccharides. Glycosaminoglycan polysaccharides can also be identified by means of their susceptibility to hydrolysis by specific enzymes or nitrous acid (Table IX). Note that only keratan sulfate is not sensitive to enzymatic or nitrous acid degradation.

TABLE IX

STABILITY OF GLYCOSAMINOGLYCAN

	Sensitive	Insensitive
Testicular hyalurondase[a] or chondroitinase AC[b]	Hyaluronate, chondroitin, chondroitin sulfates 4 and 6	Dermatan sulfate, heparin, heparan sulfate, keratan sulfate
Chondroitinase ABC[b]	Hyaluronate, chondroitin, chondroitin sulfates 4 and 6, dermatan sulfate	Heparin, heparan sulfate, keratan sulfate
Streptococcal hyaluronidase[c]	Hyaluronate and chondroitin	All sulfated glycosaminoglycans
Leech hyaluronidase[d]	Hyaluronate	Chondroitin and all sulfated glycosaminoglycans
Nitrous acid[e]	Heparin and heparan sulfate	Hyaluronate, chondroitin, chondroitin sulfates 4 and 6, dermatan sulfate, and keratan sulfate

[a] Duran-Reynols F., (1950).
[b] Yamagata et al. (1968); Saito et al. (1968).
[c] Linker et al. (1960).
[d] Meyer et al. (1960).
[e] Cifonelli (1968); Lindahl (1970).

Glycosaminoglycan polysaccharides can also be identified by their constituent disaccharides and monosaccharides. Chondroitinase ABC digestion of chrondroitin sulfates 4 and 6 liberates ΔDi4S and ΔDi6S disaccharides, respectively, which can be separated by paper chromatography (Yamagata et al., 1968; Robinson and Dorfman, 1969). Monosaccharides obtained by standard acid hydrolysis conditions can be identified by paper electrophoresis or chromatography, or chromatography on an automatic amino acid analyzer. However, N-acetylhexosamines will be degraded by the acid hydrolysis to hexosamines, making it impossible to distinguish between hexosamines and their N-acetylated derivates. Hence galactosamine in a hydrolysate could be galactosamine from keratan sulfate or N-acetylgalactosamine from chondroitin sulfate. This ambiguity could be avoided for some glycosaminoglycan polysaccharides by obtaining monosaccharides released by the combined digestion by an aminohexosidase and β-glucuronidase. Even so, identification of glycosaminoglycans on the basis of enzymatically liberated mono and disaccharides presents other ambiguities. For example, ΔDi4S could be liberated from both chondroitin 4-sulfate or dermatan sulfate by chondroitinase ABC digestion. Similarly, N-acetyl-4-glucosamine could be derived enzymatically from heparin, heparan sulfate, or hyaluronate. Therefore, analyses of monosaccharide or disaccharides of glycosaminoglycan cannot alone distinguish between different types of glycosaminoglycan polysaccharide. It is necessary to combine monosaccharide or disaccharide analyses with an additional mode of characterization, such as determination of electrophoretic mobility.

B. ANALYSIS OF SYNTHESIS OF EXTRACELLULAR MATRIX MOLECULES

Synthetic analyses generally employ procedures established for bulk analysis to determine the character of macromolecules made during a discrete time period. Although the analytical procedures used are similar, if not identical, the results of synthetic analyses must be interpreted differently from those of bulk analysis owing to fundamental differences in the nature of these two forms of analysis.

Synthesis cannot be equated with composition, in the absence of knowledge of existing composition or relative degradation of different components. While synthetic analysis may define genotypic expression, it may provide little insight into the actual phenotype. For example, consider two components made at identical rates, but degraded at drastically different rates, one five times faster than the other. Independent of the existing composition, the component turning over more slowly will represent 83% and the component turning over more rapidly 17% of what is *added* to the existing matrix even though synthetic analysis would suggest equal addition of both components. Even if the composition of the matrix was constant and not changing with time, the results of the synthetic analysis would not resemble the actual matrix composition. If three, four or even five independent components are considered, the possible total disparity between the results of synthetic and bulk analysis would be difficult to reconcile.

Synthesis has been studied in at least three different ways. Collagen made during a particular period has been determined by making the tissue or animal lathyritic for that period and analyzing the salt-soluble collagen (for example, see Miller *et al.*, 1967; Glimcher *et al.*, 1969). Synthesis of cartilage glycosaminoglycan polysaccharide has been studied by isolating chondrocytes from their matrix and analyzing the total matrix accumulated when they are grown in monolayer (for example, see Schulman and Meyer, 1968, 1970). Last, both collagen and glycosaminoglycan polysaccharide synthesis have been studied *in vivo* and *in vitro* by the incorporation of specific labeled precursors for a prescribed period.

In the first two examples, collagen and glycosaminoglycan polysaccharide were analyzed as described for analysis of total composition. In the third example, the properties of the radioactive macromolecules are directly compared to those of known composition.

1. Synthetic Analysis Using Radioactive Precursors

Measuring synthesis by the incorporation of labeled precursors presents certain problems not encountered in the determination of total composition. When there is little metabolic interconversion of labeled precursors over reasonably short incubation periods, the interpretation of precursor utilization is straightforward. One must also ascertain that equimolar amounts of the same labeled precursor are incorporated into different macromolecules or that the ratios are corrected if one is to compare relative macromolecule synthesis on the basis of relative counts.

Isotopic precursors commonly used for labeling glycosaminoglycan polysaccharide can label a variety of monosaccharide precursor pools at different specific activities, leading to large quantitative *and* qualitative errors in the estimation of relative synthesis of different glycosaminoglycan polysaccharides. For example (Fig. 3), glucosamine-^{3}H can label both UDP-N-acetylglucosamine and UDP-N-acetylgalactosamine, which would be incorporated into hyaluronate and chondroitin sulfates 4 and 6, respectively. Assuming a hypothetical situation with equal levels of hyaluronate and chondroitin sulfate actually synthesized, if the UDP-N-acetylglucosamine pool were labeled by glucosamine-^{3}H to a 10-fold greater specificity activity than the UDP-N-acetylgalactosamine pool, simple measurement of radioactivity would make it appear that chondroitin sulfate was made at one tenth the level of hyaluronate. It is not difficult to imagine how it might be possible to fail to detect synthesis of a minor component which was incorporating a monosaccharide labeled to a relatively low specific activity.

When labeling with radioglucose or galactose, the potential for error increases since these compounds can label both glucuronate and iduronate in addition to hexosamines (see Fig. 3). Finally, acetate (see Fig. 3) can label glucuronate, iduronate, hexosamine carbon backbone as well as hexosamine N-acetyl groups. It can also be incorporated into different monosaccharide precursors at various specific activities. Thus, its relative incorporation into different glycosaminoglycan polysaccharides may provide a quantitatively and qualitatively erroneous profile. To use these labeled precursors for studying relative synthesis of different glycosaminoglycan polysaccharides, it is necessary to measure the specific activities of relevant UDP-monosaccharide precursor pools.

The above discussion applies to studies of synthesis of glycosamino-

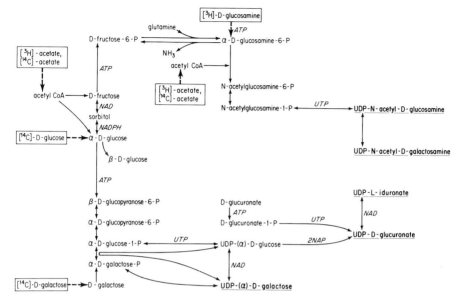

FIG. 3. Utilization of exogenous precursors.

glycan polysaccharides in only *one* tissue at only *one* time in development. In order to detect true temporal changes, or to compare synthesis in one tissue with that in other tissues at any time in development, it is necessary to measure the different monosaccharide pool specific activities for any labeled precursor.

The comparison of $^{35}SO_4{}^{2-}$ labeling of different glycosaminoglycan polysaccharides is much easier, as all molecules incorporate $^{35}SO_4{}^{2-}$ from a single pool after the monosaccharides have been polymerized into a polysaccharide chain. The use of $^{35}SO_4{}^{2-}$ to label sulfated glycosaminoglycans obviates many of the pool-related problems, since all sulfated polysaccharides incorporate $^{35}SO_4{}^{2-}$ from a single pool. Although pool problems are not encountered, other difficulties exist.

Relative $^{35}SO_4{}^{2-}$ incorporation does not reflect relative macromolecule synthesis if different molecules contain different concentrations of $SO_4{}^{2-}$. Chondroitin sulfate, keratan sulfate, dermatan sulfate, heparin and heparan sulfate do not contain the same relative levels of $SO_4{}^{2-}$. Also early embryonic chick tissues synthesize different proportions of *partially* and fully sulfated chondroitin sulfates, depending both on the tissue and the developmental age (see Kvist and Finnegan, 1970; Manasek *et al.*, 1973). Thus, it is necessary to obtain a measure of the relative levels of sulfation in order to make any quantitative comparison on the basis of ^{35}S labeling. In this laboratory, different levels for sulfation of chondroitin sulfates have been suggested by different relative electrophoretic mobilities. For example, fully sulfated chondroitin sulfate migrates faster than partially sulfated chondroitin sulfate, and heparin migrates faster than heparan sulfate. Electrophoretic mobility alone does not provide the quantitative data necessary for determination of relative degrees of sulfation. Obviously, the relative migration of different molecular species (e.g., heparan sulfate vs chondroitin sulfate) may not only reflect relative sulfation, but be a function of size and composition as well.

Finally, it is important to note that a large number of synthetic studies have employed isolated tissues or cells incubated with labeled precursors *in vitro*. Many of these studies have failed to demonstrate that the product made *in vitro* was the same as that made *in vivo*. This demonstration of synthetic homology is especially crucial for embryonic tissues and cells in view of their plasticity and sensitivity to environmental influences (Layman *et al.*, 1972).

IV. Anatomical and Structural Considerations of the Embryonic Extracellular Matrix

The extracellular matrix occupies all the embryonic space that is not occupied by cells or lumina. As such, it extends to the basal plasmalemmas of epithelia, includes the basal lamina, completely surrounds mesenchyme, and includes mesenchymal cell surface costs.

A. LIGHT MICROSCOPY

Very little structure can be seen in the extracellular matrix of embryos with the light microscope, and, in routine histological preparations, these regions appear to be either "empty" or to contain only traces of filamentous material. Perhaps this is why so little attention has been given the extracellular matrix in classical embryology.

B. ELECTRON MICROSCOPY

Electron microscope observations of embryonic extracellular matrices also do not provide many data that are useful in determining the composition of early embryonic extracellular matrix. In chick embryos prior to about stage 10— (about 9 somites, 32 hours of incubation), the electron microscope reveals the presence of three general classes of electron-dense matrix components: unbanded fibrils, amorphous dense bodies, and developing basal laminae; in each case their composition is unknown.

1. Matrix Fibrils

Fibrils, prior to about stage 10— (9 somites, 32 hours of incubation) appear as thin filaments, initially with a diameter of 40–45 Å, termed "primary" fibrils (Low, 1968). A second class of filament, termed the microfibril (Low, 1968), with diameters of 45–150 Å, appears to delaminate from basal laminae. In the perinotochordal sheath, these fibrils are sensitive to both trypsin and collagenase digestion (Fredrickson and Low, 1971), but although smaller fibrils (100 Å or less in diameter) are sensitive to trypsin, hyaluronidase, α-amylase (Fredrickson and Low, 1971) they resist digestion by collagenase. Low (1968), solely on the basis of ultrastructural studies, postulated that all mature connective tissue fibers (e.g., collagen, elastic, and reticular fibers) arise by means of coalescence and modification of the more primitive "primary" microfibril.

2. Amorphous Material

The second type of electron dense matrix inclusion is the amorphous dense material termed "interstitial body" by Low (1970). It is present either in isolated clumps or in association with basal laminae (Low, 1970; Johnson et al., 1974). Although widespread throughout the entire early embryonic matrix in isolated patches, occasional areas show extensive accumulations of dense material (Johnson et al., 1974).

3. Basal Laminae

Basal laminae are dense filamentous layers, visible with the electron microscope, that underlie epithelia. These sheets of material, about 500–900 Å thick (in mature systems), consist of an electron-lucent (lamina rara) and an electron-dense portion (lamina densa).

Basal laminae are already seen along the basal surface of the chick embryo epiblast at the time the egg is laid (Low, 1967). Such early lamina are generally devoid of the lamina rara, which is characteristic of more mature basal laminae, and are often discontinuous. By 12 hours of incubation the epiblast basal lamina has become more discrete except in the region of the primitive streak, where it remains absent (Low, 1967). With continued incubation, basal laminae develop along other embryonic epithelial basal surfaces and generally follow the same developmental sequence: an initial discontinuous electron dense material gradually becomes continuous concomitantly with the appearance of the lamina rara (Low, 1967; Johnson et al., 1974).

4. Cell Surface Coats

Mature cells are surrounded by a layer of extracellular material, usually called a cell coat (see Bennett, 1963; Rambourg et al., 1966; Pease, 1966). In routine light and electron microscope preparations very little of the cell coat is visible, and consequently cell surfaces were largely ignored until the development and application of special techniques to demonstrate the coat. Although the structure of these coats, as seen with the electron microscope, gives no clue as to their composition, special training techniques do. Mature cell coats contain carbohydrate as determined by the periodic acid-Schiff (PAS) reaction (Leblond, 1950). These carbohydrates are linked to protein to form glycoproteins (Section II, C). Cell coats stain with PA–silver methenamine and the PTA-low pH technique (Rambourg and Leblond, 1967; Rambourg, 1969) techniques known to demonstrate glycoproteins (Rambourg, 1971). Additionally, cationic dyes, such as ruthenium red (Luft, 1971), bind to the surface coats, thus indicating the presence of acidic groups. The techniques currently employed to demonstrate morphologically the presence of cell coats are thus dependent upon the use of relatively discrete histochemical techniques. Consequently microscopic examination of cell coats provides information about their composition.

Despite the seemingly ubiquitous distribution of surface coats in cells of mature organisms, relatively little is know about their presence and distribution in intact embryos. Martínez-Palomo (1970) has detected a ruthenium red-positive coat along the basal surface of chick ectoderm at the primitive streak stage. Mesenchyme and endoderm stained in similar fashion. In this laboratory we noted marked regional variation in the distribution of ruthenium red-positive cell coats. For example, although the apical surface of the mycardium of stage 12 chick embryos stained very heavily (Fig. 4; see also Martínez-Palomo, 1970), other epithelial surfaces, such as portions of endoderm and some mesenchymal surfaces, did not bind detectable amounts of ruthenium red. Lesseps (1967) showed the presence of lanthanum-staining material on the surface of embryonic chick heart, neural retina and limb bud cells, but did not actually identify the precise cell type he was examining, nor was any attempt made to determine whether these cell coats change during development.

Ruthenium red-positive cell coats are sensitive to a number of agents (Huet and Herzberg, 1973). This sensitivity varies among cultured cells that are manipulated differently. This suggests that the surface coat may be a physiologically sensitive structure that changes in response to external conditions. A recent discussion of some aspects of cell surface coats and their properties has appeared (Revel and Goodenough, 1970).

C. ANATOMICAL CORRELATES OF BIOCHEMICAL ANALYSES

It is virtually impossible to identify accurately the extracellular location or cellular origin of extracellular matrix solely on the basis of biochemical analysis. In order to derive these morphological correlates, recourse to histochemical or radioautographic technique is called for. Al-

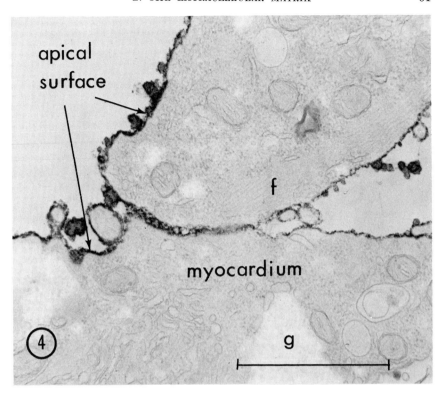

apical
surface

f

myocardium

4   g

Fig. 4. Embryonic cell coats can be demonstrated electron microscopically after staining with ruthenium red, a dye that binds to polyanions. This section of differentiated myocardium of a stage 12- embryo shows the presence of a cell coat on developing cardiac myocytes. The apical (outer) surface of the heart is particularly reactive. Although not counterstained, myofibrils (f) and pools of glycogen (g) are recognizable. Calibration equals 1 μm.

though electron microscope examination reveals the presence of a number of matrix inclusions, the composition of any of these early embryonic substances cannot be deduced from their appearance alone.

1. Localization of Collagen

We cannot at this time say whether *any* of the electron dense components of the extracellular matrix seen in very young embryos represents early embryonic collagen. Not until unequivocally crossbanded collagen fibrils appear in the matrix can morphological criteria be used alone to identify this component. In the chick embryo, crossbanded collagen fibrils can be identified in the developing heart by stage 10- (9 somites) (Johnson et al., 1974) and also around the neural tube at a slightly later time (Fig. 5). Although such observations determine the *presence* of collagen, they tell us nothing about its synthesis or even composition and/or type. As we shall see in later sections, synthesis of the various types of collagens begins much earlier in development.

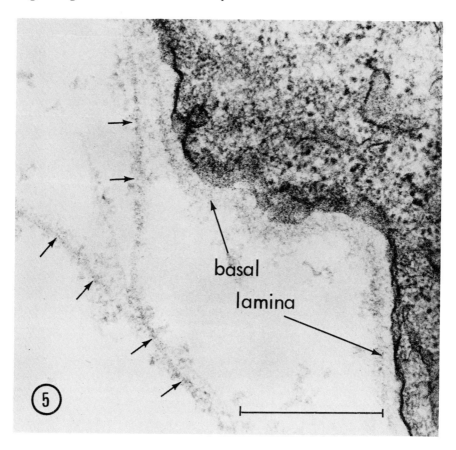

FIG. 5. In stage 10+ chick embryos, the neural tube already has a well formed basal lamina. It is often associated with fibrillar collagen (arrows) embedded in the surrounding matrix. These observations on a normal tissue *in situ* show that a number of morphologically recognizable components of the matrix are synthesized early in development. Calibration equals 0.5 μm.

The presence of crossbanding does not permit identification of collagen type, since under appropriate fixation conditions even Type II collagen of cartilage demonstrates crossbanding (Fig. 6). Collagen of the guinea pig epiphysial plate demonstrates clear crossbanding if the cartilage is treated with papain (Thyberg *et al.*, 1973). Moreover, Type I collagen synthesis is detectable biochemically in very young embryos

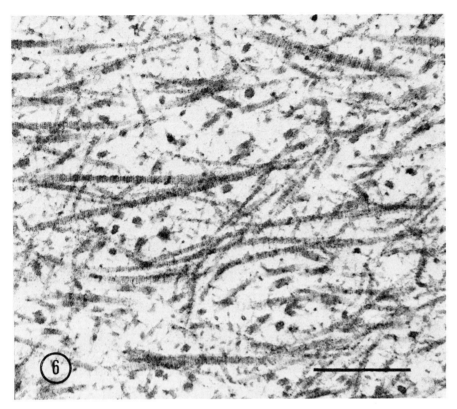

FIG. 6. Type II collagen is crossbanded. When mouse articular cartilage is fixed according to Hirsch and Fedorko (1968), each fibril shows discrete crossbanding. Micrograph by courtesy of Dr. Marijke Holtrop. Calibration equals 0.5 μm.

prior to detection of crossbanded fibrils. Thus, reliance upon electron microscopic detection of crossbanded fibrils is meaningless either as an index of Type I collagen synthesis or as a guide to its distribution in young embryos. Type IV collagen has been isolated only from a few unique forms of basal lamina. Since it comprises only a portion of the basal lamina its morphological appearance cannot be deduced. Perhaps it indeed represents the thin, filamentous material of the lamina dense, but this remains unproved. Furthermore, Type IV collagen has not been shown to be a universal component of basal laminae, and it may be erroneous to assume that visualization of basal lamina is indicative of the presence of any form of collagen, even Type IV. Even with routine fixation procedures, crossbanded collagen fibrils can be detected in very close association with (or embedded in) normal developing basal laminae (see Johnson et al., 1974).

It is not known whether all developing basal laminae are similar in composition, whether tissue-specific differences exist, or whether major ontogenic changes occur in composition. Pierce and his colleagues (see Pierce, 1970) have demonstrated the presence of a common antigenic site in several basal laminae suggesting some compositional similarities. Fucose-containing glycoproteins are synthesized and secreted at the time the basal lamina first appears in the embryonic heart (Manasek, in preparation). One or more of these glycoproteins are localized in the developing basal lamina, particularly in the dense regions (Manasek, 1975). Martínez-Palomo (1970) showed that the basal lamina of epiblast binds ruthenium red and that the adjacent cell membrane also binds ruthenium red. Recent histochemical studies (Trelstad et al., 1974; Hay and Meier, 1974) have also demonstrated the presence of anionic sites in a variety of embryonic basal laminae at a time when the associated epithelia are synthesizing glycosaminoglycans. This is in accord with other studies suggesting the presence of glycosaminoglycans within other embryonic basal laminae (Bernfield et al., 1972). Anionic sites are present also in very early embryonic cardiac laminae when they are just beginning to form (Manasek, 1975), and radioautographic studies of synthesis show a concentration of sulfated glycosaminoglycans over these ontogenetically early laminae also (Johnston and Comar, 1957; Manasek, 1970, 1973). It is interesting to note that colloidal thorium does not bind to early cardiac basal laminae (Johnson et al., 1974) that do bind some ruthenium red (Manasek, 1975). The anionic sites appear to be relatively weak.

Radioautography, using proline-^{3}H as a precursor, is often used to localize collagen synthesis. Although collagen synthesis can be detected by this means, proline will also be incorporated into a number of other proteins. Of particular interest is the finding that core protein of chondroitin sulfate contains large amounts of proline. Collagen is usually found in conjunction with some amount of chondroitin sulfate, hence the interpretation of such radioautographic data are questionable. For example, embryonic fibrillar collagen is often surrounded by intensely ruthenium red-positive material reminiscent of chondromucoprotein (Fig. 7; see also discussion by Bernfield et al., 1973).

2. Histochemical Demonstration of Glycosaminoglycans

Histochemical procedures designed to identify and localize glycosaminoglycans are, in general, tedious and have not been applied widely to embryonic material. No attempt can be made here to discuss more than a small fraction of the many procedures that have been devised (see Spicer et al., 1967) and applied to early developing embryos.

Detection of metachromasia (Schubert and Hamerman, 1956) and

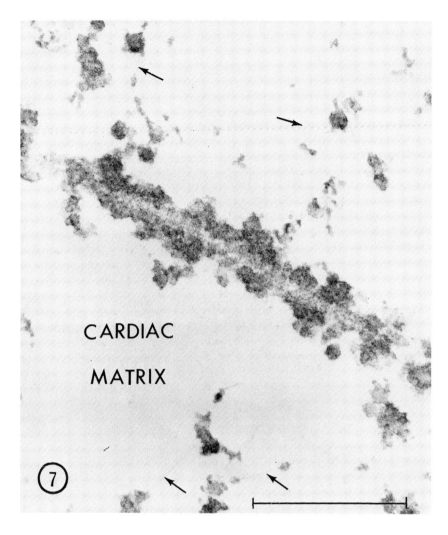

FIG. 7. Collagen and glycosaminoglycans are intimately related. The cardiac matrix of stage 10 embryonic chicks shows ruthenium red-positive material intimately associated with fibrillar collagen. Despite the lack of counterstaining, cross banding is evident. Clumps of ruthenium red-positive material are connected by thin filaments, much as they are in chondromucoprotein (arrows). Calibration equals 0.5 μm.

alcianophilia do not by themselves identify the type of mucosubstance present. Combinations of Alcian blue and periodic acid–Schiff techniques (Spicer, 1960), Alcian blue–aldehyde fuchsin (see Spicer, 1963) are particularly useful and have been applied to histochemical studies of the developing axial regions (Kvist and Finnegan, 1970). Of particular interest is the "critical electrolyte concentration" technique in which Alcian blue 8GX is dissolved in various concentrations of buffered $MgCl_2$ (Scott and Dorling, 1965). Different mucosubstances will bind either dye (hence become visible) or Mg^{2+} (hence remain unstained) at different salt concentrations. This technique has been used in studies of rat heart mucosubstances (Markwald and Adams Smith, 1972) and somite development in the chick (O'Hare, 1973). Use of blocking methods (Quintarelli et al., 1964) to complement the above techniques aids markedly in improving the reliability of identifying sulfated mucosubstances.

The lower limits of resolution in histochemical studies may not be adequate for the study of developing systems. For example, O'Hare (1973) was unable to detect sulfated mucosubstances associated with chick embryo somites prior to stage 14, yet earlier biochemical studies (Franco-Browder et al., 1963) clearly established their presence. Therefore, a negative histochemical reaction must be interpreted with caution. A positive reaction can provide useful information concerning *localization* of material, but generally cannot be relied upon to identify the cells or tissues of origin, since accumulation of material rather than synthesis is being demonstrated. Furthermore, the uncertainty involving the composition of matrix at early stages makes interpretation of histochemical results difficult (see discussion in Kvist and Finnegan, 1970).

The regional distribution of some glycosaminoglycans early in development has been determined histochemically. For example, aside from the obvious localization of chondroitin sulfate in developing cartilage, particularly developing perinotochordal sclerotome (Kvist and Finnegan, 1970), unsulfated glycosaminoglycan (either hyaluronate or chondroitin) was found associated with all axial structures. Surprisingly, the concentration of hyaluronate increased with development in both the neural tube and the chondrogenic sclerotome (Kvist and Finnegan, 1970).

V. Extracellular Matrices through Gastrulation

In the preceding sections some of the basic characteristics of extracellular macromolecules as well as ways to analyze them have been described. The following sections will consider the matrix of developing embryos. Initially, we shall examine matrices of young embryos prior to establishment of histologically recognizable "connective tissues," such as cartilage. No distinction can be made in early embryos between "connective tissue" and nonconnective tissue extracellular matrices on the basis of appearance or types of macromolecules synthesized. Embryos contain extracellular matrix prior to establishment of morphologically detectable mesoderm. Despite the fact that mesoderm gives rise to much of what is considered to be "connective tissue" in mature organisms, extracellular matrix production is not the principal function of this or any other germ layer during early development.

A. GLYCOSAMINOGLYCANS

Early extracellular regions stain metachromatically, suggesting the presence of a high density of negative charges, such as those of polyanionic glycosaminoglycans. (see also Franco-Browder et al., 1963). Early radioautographic studies clearly showed the utilization of inorganic sulfur in the synthesis of extracellular material. Johnston and Comar (1957) injected radiosulfur into unincubated chick eggs and examined distribution of label radioautographically at different times following incubation. This method of isotope administration has severe shortcomings. Each stage examined has been, in effect, incubated in the presence of isotope for a different amount of time, making direct comparison impossible; with older embryos, the long incubation periods mean that the location of extracellular label does not necessarily reflect region of synthesis, but rather of final deposition. Furthermore, since grain density increases with length of incubation, small changes in synthesis will become more difficult to detect. Nonetheless, this study still represents one of the most thorough analyses of sulfur incorporation by intact chick embryos.

Two major findings of this study are that every tissue of young embryos incorporates inorganic sulfur and that, determined by grain density, distribution of label is uniform up to about stage 3 (approximately 12 hours of incubation). From stage 3+ on, sulfur incorporation demonstrated progressively greater regional differences. These studies made the fundamental observation that regional differences in matrix production could be discerned prior to any clear-cut histodifferentiation. These differences occurred prior to so-called "connective tissue" differentiation. Furthermore, these studies indicated that each cell, at least during very early development, is active in the production of sulfated matrix. This does not mean that each cell goes through a "connective tissue" phase before differentiating, but simply shows that production of some extracellular materials may not be a specialized function.

Both $^{35}SO_4^{2-}$ and ^{14}C-labeled amino acid uptake during early sea urchin development was examined by Immers (1961), who demonstrated radioautographically the incorporation of both labels into extracellular material. $^{35}SO_4^{2-}$ utilization appeared first at the blastula stage and is most intense around the vegetal region of the blastocoele.

More recently, Kosher and Searls (1973) have reexamined radiosulfur utilization *in vivo* in frog embryos. Sulfur incorporation was detected even in unfertilized eggs. They detected sulfur incorporation into two glycosaminoglycans: heparin/heparan sulfate and chondroitin sulfate. At stages 2–9 no detectable chondroitin 6-sulfate was being made, but incorporated sulfur label appeared principally (82%) in heparan sulfate/heparin and chondroitin 4-sulfate. With development, embryos began to utilize exogenous ^{35}S in the synthesis of chondroitin 6-sulfate. As measurable amounts of labeled chondroitin 6-sulfate began to appear, the relative amount of label in chondroitin 4-sulfate and heparan sulfate/heparin declined. These investigations identified clearly the presence of the chondroitin sulfate type molecule and the heparan sulfate/heparin type of molecule.

The relative $^{35}SO_4{}^{2-}$ labeling of chondroitin sulfate and heparan sulfate/heparin observed may not reflect actual relative amounts of sulfated glycosaminoglycan polysaccharide made since the levels of sulfation of these different species were not compared. Although much of the $^{35}SO_4{}^{2-}$-labeled glycosaminoglycan polysaccharide in early embryos was identified as heparan sulfate/heparin, the high grain density surrounding intracellular yolk platelets seen autoradiographically make it difficult to interpret these observations in terms of early embryonic matrix, especially for chick embryos whick lack similar intracellular yolk platelets. If one assumes that heparan sulfate/heparin are mainly intracellular in early embryonic tissues (as appears to be the case for more mature tissues) one might interpret Kosher and Searls' observations as describing a change in extracellular matrix sulfated glycosaminoglycans from only chondroitin 4-sulfate to chondroitin 4-sulfate and 6-sulfate synthesis with synthesis of the 6-isomer accompanied by the appearance of relative increases in $^{35}SO_4{}^{2-}$ labeling in areas such as the chordamesoderm.

1. Sulfated Glycosaminoglycans in Early Chick Development

With intact chick embryos grown in New (1955) cultures, it was possible to demonstrate synthesis of sulfated glycosaminoglycans in primitive streak stage chick embryos. Both the area opaca and area pellucida synthesize sulfated glycosaminoglycans, which were characterized by electrophoretic mobility of papin-digested $^{35}SO_4{}^{2-}$-labeled material and sensitivity to both testicular hyaluronidase and nitrous acid (see Table IX).

Both area opaca and area pellucida synthesize undersulfated chondroitin sulfate (Figs. 8 and 9), but only the area opaca synthesizes fully sulfated chondroitin sulfate (peak I, Fig. 8). The testicular hyaluronidase-resistant component of peak II (Figs. 8 and 9) was shown to be heparan sulfate (Table X) on the basis of nitrous acid sensitivity.

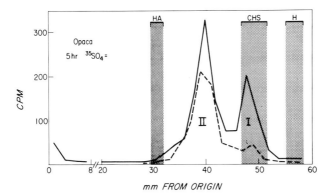

FIG. 8. Figures 8 through 11 represent electrophoretic migration of labeled glycos-aminoglycans. In all cases, the technique is identical to that described by Manasek *et al.* (1973). Sulfated material synthesized by area opaca electrophoresis as two distinct peaks (solid lines). Peak I comigrates with authentic chondroitin sulfate and is largely sensitive to testicular hyaluronidase (dashed line represents insensitive material). Further analysis shows the sensitive portion to be chondroitin 4-sulfate and the resistant to be either keratan or dermatan sulfate. Peak II is largely insensitive to testicular hyaluronidase (dashed line). This material is heparan sulfate. The difference between the dashed and solid line represents undersulfated chondroitin 4-sulfate. No sulfated material comigrates with standard hyaluronate (HA) or heparin (H).

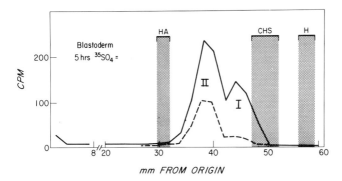

FIG. 9. The blastoderm (area pellucida) also makes sulfated glycosaminoglycans but no peak comigrates with fully sulfated authentic chondroitin sulfate. Peak I is largely testicular hyaluronidase sensitive (dashed line) and contains undersulfated chondroitin-4-sulfate. Peak I from area pellucida does not coelectrophorese with peak I from opaca (Fig. 8), but peaks II coelectrophorese. The testicular hyaluronidase-resistant material in peak II (dashed line) represents heparan sulfate.

Chondroitin sulfate was removed by digestion with testicular hyaluronidase (see Figs. 8 and 9) and the remaining material (which would be expected to contain the heparin and/or heparan sulfate and, if present, dermatan or keratan sulfate) was subjected to nitrous acid degradation.

TABLE X

CHARACTERIZATION OF SULFATED GLYCOSAMINOGLYCANS (GAGs) BY SELECTIVE
LOSS OF SULFUR-35 (PRIMITIVE STREAK STAGE CHICK EMBRYOS)

| | | ^{35}S counts per minute | |
Material subjected to HNO$_2$ digestion	Source	Nitrous acid sensitive (heparan sulfate)	Nitrous acid resistant
Total GAGs labeled	Area opaca	13,000	160,000
with $^{35}SO_4{}^{2-}$	Blastoderm	2,000	19,000
Testicular hyaluronidase-	Area opaca	20,700	2,600
resistant GAGs labeled	Blastoderm	2,200	0
with $^{35}SO_4{}^{2-}$			

It was not possible to detect any nitrous acid-resistant material synthesized by embryos (Table X) but a small amount of sulfated glycosaminoglycans synthesized by the opaca resisted nitrous acid (Table X). This fraction represents either dermatan or keratan sulfate (chondroitin sulfate 4/6 was already removed by testicular hyaluronidase).

Chick embryo chondroitin sulfates were characterized further by treatment with chondroitinase ABC to yield ΔDi4S and ΔDi6S moieties. Despite the differences in sulfation of the chondroitin sulfate made by area opaca and area pellucida (see Figs. 8 and 9), chondroitin 4-sulfate was the only isomer whose synthesis was detected (Table XI). By stages 9–11, chick embryos that are now making fully sulfated chondroitin sulfate (Manasek et al., 1973) are still synthesizing principally chondroitin 4-sulfate. If chondroitin 6-sulfate is being made, it is synthesized in amounts below the limit of resolution (Table XI).

TABLE XI

CHROMATOGRAPHIC SEPARATION OF ΔDI4-S AND ΔDI6-S
MOIETIES FROM ^{35}S-LABELED CHONDROITIN SULFATE

| | Counts per minute | | |
Source (chick embryo)	Origin	ΔDi4S	ΔDi6S
Area opaca (stages 4–7)	29	2400	26
Area pellucida (stages 4–7)	28	680	27
Embryo (stages 9–11)	33	1260	26

Because nitrous acid sensitivity of both total sulfated glycosamino-glycans and of those resistant to testicular hyaluronidase were examined, we can, by subtraction, determine the relative distribution of sulfur label in different glycosaminoglycans (Table XII). It is stressed that these

TABLE XII

DISTRIBUTION OF INCORPORATED SULFUR-35 INTO DIFFERENT
GLYCOSAMINOGLYCANS IN PRIMITIVE STREAK CHICK EMBRYOS[a]

Location	ChS 4 and 6	HS	KS, DS
Area opaca	95%	4.5%	0.5%
Area pellucida	90%	10%	—

[a] ChS, chondroitin sulfate; HS, heparan sulfate; KS, keratan sulfate; DS, dermatan sulfate.

figures represent only the distribution of the sulfur label and do not neces-sarily reflect relative amounts of different molecular species. The latter cannot be determined on the basis of sulfur labeling alone because of the different and possibly variable levels of sulfation of different molecu-lar species. Furthermore, the category "chondroitin sulfate" was defined enzymatically as that fraction sensitive to testicular hyaluronidase. The electrophoretic analysis shows that this fraction consists of fully sulfated (or, in the case of the embryo, almost fully) and distinctly undersulfated components. In frog embryos the bulk of the incorporated radiosulfur appeared in heparin/heparan sulfate (Kosher and Searls, 1973). It is not known whether this difference between frogs and chickens represents a true difference in matrix composition. Kosher and Searls found a great deal of label associated with intracellular yolk platelets, which are very prominent during early frog development and probably contain heparin/heparan sulfate.

2. *^{3}H-Glucosamine Labeled Glycosaminoglycans*

Electrophoresis of papain digests of both area pellucida and area opaca of stage 4 embryos incubated with glucosamine-^{3}H reveals a single prominent testicular hyaluronidase-sensitive peak (Figs. 10 and 11). A small amount of glucosamine-derived label is found in advance of the major peak and appears as two much smaller peaks that coelectrophorese with chondroitin sulfate and heparan sulfate. Each of these minor peaks contains less than 10% of the total glucosamine-derived label (insets, Figs. 10 and 11).

Total glycosaminoglycans were precipitated with CPC and hydro-

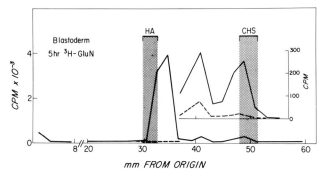

Fig. 10. Tritiated glucosamine labels glycosaminoglycans in primitive streak stages, but the bulk of the label appears in a major peak migrating near authentic hyaluronate. This material is entirely sensitive to testicular hyaluronidase digestion (dashed lines). Two smaller peaks are present; they are shown more clearly in inset. Dashed lines represent material insensitive to testicular hyaluronidase. The pattern of enzyme sensitivity, electrophoretic mobility, and hexosamine analysis (Fig. 12) shows the material in the major peak to be hyaluronate. Glucosamine clearly labels hyaluronate preferentially.

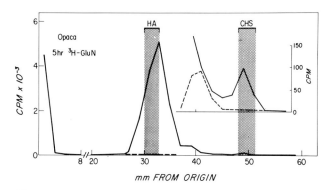

Fig. 11. The area opaca also makes hyaluronate, and glucosamine preferentially labels this glycosaminoglycan. Relatively little (<100 cpm) label appears to coelectrophorese with chondroitin sulfate (inset). As expected, label does appear as testicular hyaluronidase insensitive (dashed lines) heparan sulfate.

lyzed with 4 N HCl *in vacuo* at 100°C. Individual amino sugars were separated on an amino acid analyzer. In material from both area opaca and blastoderm, the principal labeled amino sugar was glucosamine (Fig. 12). Less than 10% of incorporated label appeared in galactosamine (Fig. 12A and B). This is further evidence that the principal glucosamine-labeled electrophoretic peak is hyaluronate. These analyses show that hyaluronate is present and is being synthesized as early as the primitive streak stages of chick development. Moreover, it is not restricted to the

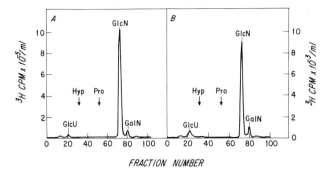

FRACTION NUMBER

Fig. 12. After incubation with ³H-labeled glucosamine, tissue was digested with papain, glycosaminoglycans were precipitated with cetyl pyridinium chloride (CPC) and hydrolyzed, and hexosamines were separated on an automatic amino acid analyzer. Label in both opaca (A) and pellucida (B) is principally glucosamine, indicating that the principal peaks shown in Fig. 10 and 11 are hyaluronate. Small amounts of labeled galactosamine are recovered, consistent with the electrophoretic and enzymatic identification of small amounts of labeled chondroitin sulfate (Figs. 10 and 11).

structures that form the embryonic body, but is synthesized by extraembryonic tissues (in this case, the area opaca) as well.

It was not possible to determine directly the relative synthesis of hyaluronate, heparan sulfate, and chondroitin sulfate on a mass, or molar, basis. Because chondroitin sulfate exists as both a fully sulfated and partially sulfated molecule, and in this case heparan sulfate contains fewer sulfur residues per mole than does fully sulfated chondroitin sulfate, a comparison of ³⁵S label between heparan sulfate and chondroitin sulfate will not necessarily indicate relative molar amounts of synthesis. Moreover, since chondroitin sulfate contains N-acetylgalactosamine and hyaluronate contains N-acetylglucosamine as the amino sugar, one cannot use glucosamine-³H derived label incorporation into hyaluronate and chondroitin sulfate to show true relative rates of synthesis. Incorporation of label is a function of pool specific activity, and the specific activities of N-acetylgalactosamine and N-acetylglucosamine pools were not determined.

Incorporation of glucosamine-³H into hyaluronate and heparan sulfate can be used to indicate relative synthesis. Hyaluronate consists of a repeating sequence of N-acetyl-D-glucosamine and glucuronate. The polysaccharide moiety of heparan sulfate consists of N-acetyl-D-glucosamine and iduronate. These glycosaminoglycans have a common precursor subunit, N-acetyl-D-glucosamine, which, presumably for synthesis of both glycosaminoglycans, comes from the same pool. Irrespective of N-acetyl-D-glucosamine pool specific activity the incorporation of this

precursor subunit into hyaluronate and heparan sulfate will reflect relative rates of synthesis. Based on electrophoretic separation of glycosaminoglycans, it is estimated that less than 3% of total incorporated
glucosamine-derived label appears in heparan sulfate. Heparan sulfate
synthesis is less than 3% of that of hyaluronate.

3. The Localization of Glycosaminoglycans

Since more than 90% of glucosamine-derived label appears in hyaluronate, one expects that silver grains of radioautographs of glucosa-
mine-^{3}H-incubated material would represent hyaluronate with a 0.9 probability. This probability is, in all likelihood, somewhat lower since an
unknown amount of glucosamine may be utilized in the production of
glycoproteins.

Glucosamine uptake by young (stage 4 to stage 5) chick embryos
was examined radioautographically. Label, after a 6-hour incubation, is
particularly intense over all cells (Fig. 13) and also over the intercellular
spaces of epithelia, such as neural plate and ectoderm. Thus, in presomite
chick embryos, radioautography shows that glucosamine-derived label
is restricted largely to intraepithelial intercellular spaces and the region

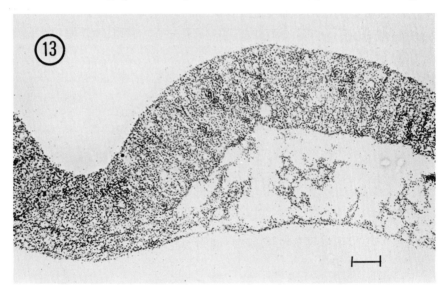

Fig. 13. Incubation of a stage 4 chick embryo with ^{3}H-labeled glucosamine permits
the biochemical demonstration of hyaluronate synthesis. Radioautographs show that
most label is intimately associated with cells; especially the intercellular spaces
of the ectoderm. In this respect distribution of glucosamine-derived label is different
than sulfate label. Addition of CPC to the fixative does not alter the apparent
distribution. Calibration equals 20 μm.

of mesenchyme cell surfaces. To be sure, some of this radioautographi-cally detected label may represent glycoprotein, but a substantial amount must also represent the hyaluronate detected biochemically. Taken col-lectively, these observations suggest that in early embryos hyaluronate is closely associated with developing cells. In slightly older embryos (cer-tainly by stage 7+), hyaluronate is probably more widely distributed, and large amounts of extracellular label can be detected radioautographi-cally, especially along the lateral sides of the neural tube (Fig. 14A).

Of particular interest is the observation that glucosamine incorpora-tion by a number of tissues is not uniform. In particular, the neural tube shows a marked dorsoventral gradient, with the ventral cells labeled most heavily as is the matrix surrounding the ventral regions. This gradient is most obvious at later stages (Fig. 14), and the dorsal regions of the neural tube, as well as such cells as neural crest, incorporate barely detectable amounts of label (Fig. 14 and Manasek, unpublished obser-vations). These differences do not exist for all labeled precursors. For ex-ample, fucose-6-³H is rapidly utilized by neural crest cells (Manasek, unpublished observations) suggesting that these mesenchymal cells make large amounts of glycoproteins. These observations suggest that gradients may exist for the synthesis of extracellular materials. If, for example, the dorsoventral differences seen in the neural tube are not the result of precursor pool size differences, then we must conclude that different cells of the same tissue make different contributions, both quantitatively and qualitatively, to the surrounding matrix and hence establish gradi-ents within the matrix.

Inorganic sulfur is incorporated into sulfated glycosaminoglycans (Boström and Aqvist, 1952; Amprino, 1955; Dziewiatkowski, 1958), not in other compounds that would be retained for radioautography (for dis-cussion, see Kosher and Searls, 1973). Thus, radioautographs of material labeled with $^{35}SO_4^{2-}$ can be expected to localize sites of synthesis of sul-fated glycosaminoglycans. By this criterion, each cell in chick embryos of stages 5 to 7+ is synthesizing one or more sulfated glycosaminoglycans (Fig. 15). Sulfated matrix is particularly heavy along the developing neural tube (Fig. 15), as it is in somewhat older stages (Manasek, 1970). The matrix between developing notochord and neural tube is very heavily labeled (Fig. 15). The distribution of ^{35}S in these young embryos is gen-erally quite similar to that noted in slightly older (stage 8, ca 28 hours of incubation) chick embryos (Hay, 1973). In general, the matrix imme-diately subjacent epithelia, such as ectoderm and neural tube, is labeled heavily (Fig. 15), suggesting the presence of sulfated molecules in devel-oping embryonic basal laminae, corroborating earlier findings of sulfated glycosaminoglycans in basal laminae (Bernfield et al., 1973).

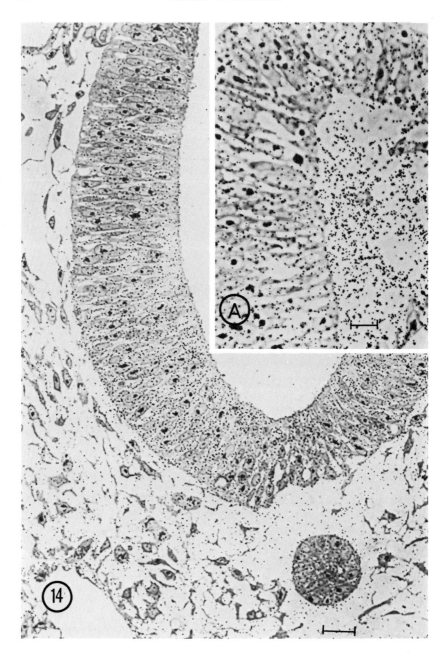

FIGS. 14, 14A. Although the bulk of the matrix remains unlabeled by a 6-hour exposure to glucosamine in stage 4 embryos (Fig. 13) 2 hours' incubation suffices to label the extracellular matrix in a stage 7+ (2 somite) embryo (Fig. 14A). By

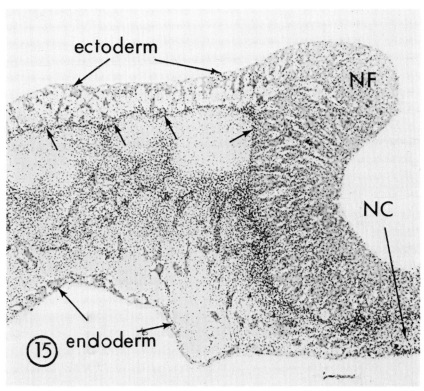

FIG. 15. This stage 7 embryo had been incubated with $^{35}SO_4^{2-}$ for 6 hours. The radioautographs show sulfated matrix to be associated with basal surfaces of epithelia (arrows) which are forming basal laminae. Heavy label is found along the basal neural tube, particularly in the regions between neural tube and developing notochord (NC) NF, neural fold; Calibration equals 20 μm.

Clearly, relating matrix changes temporally to developmental events will be a major undertaking. This will require precise quantitative analyses of matrix from different embryonic regions. In all likelihood, measurement of matrix made by very young rudiments grown in culture would not suffice since studies of cultured material may not reveal, with certainty, what similar tissues synthesize *in situ*. In addition to temporal correlations, experimental, or causal, correlations would be needed, a requirement that increases the difficulty of such a pursuit. Moreover, it

about stage 12— (15 somites) 2 hours' incubation with ^{3}H-labeled glucosamine is still adequate to label the matrix and also to demonstrate a marked dorsoventral gradient in label utilization. The region around the ventral neural tube and notochord is heavily labeled, but the dorsal regions are not. Calibrations: Fig. 14: 20 μm; Fig. 14A: 10 μm.

seems likely, on the basis of radioautographic grain distribution, that subtle quantitative differences may exist between different regions. It seems likely, therefore, that if extracellular glycosaminoglycans mediate in some way developmental events, such influence is a result of quantitative changes in matrix components rather than qualitative changes, such as the sudden appearance or disappearance of any single glycosaminoglycan.

B. COLLAGEN SYNTHESIS IN EARLY DEVELOPMENT

Studies of glycosaminoglycans discussed in the preceding section show that the matrix is heterogeneous with respect to these molecules both in terms of composition and distribution. Glycosaminoglycans are, however, not the only macromolecules present. Although electron microscope studies (discussed in Section IV, B) cannot definitively identify collagen at these early stages, and we do not know the composition of early basal laminae, there are some suggestions that collagen synthesis may be occurring. The production of radioactive hydroxyproline from exogenous labeled proline by *Xenopus laevis* (Green *et al.*, 1968) and *Rana pipiens* (Klöse and Flickinger, 1971) embryos at about the time of gastrulation suggest a very low level of collagen synthesis. In the case of *X. laevis* gastrulae, less than 1 cpm of hydroxyproline per embryo was recovered and the hydroxyproline-containing polypeptides were not characterized. If this is indeed a measure of collagen synthesis, then the levels are exceedingly low.

In this laboratory, in work with intact primitive streak chick embryos, the synthesis of collagen chains that were similar, if not identical, to those of Type I, Type III, and Type IV collagen of much more mature chick tissues has been determined.

1. Collagen Synthesis by Primitive Streak Chick Embryos

Collagen synthesis in chick embryos (or embryonic tissue) is examined routinely by labeling *in vitro* with proline-³H. Label is administered after a 1-hour preincubation with BAPN (to make newly synthesized collagen lathyritic and salt soluble) and sodium ascorbate (to assure normal proline and lysine hydroxylation) (Levenson, 1969; Peterkofsky, 1972). For early developmental stages, intact embryos (blastoderm and area opaca) were grown in New (1955) culture. Embryos develop normally under these conditions. After a 6-hour incubation with proline-³H, the area opaca and area pellucida were separated and their proline-³H-labeled proteins were extracted and analyzed separately.

Labeled protein eluted with both α1 and α2 chains from CM-cellulose as well as in a discrete peak after α1 chains, but before standard α2 chains

(Fig. 16). This pattern was similar for both the embryo (area pellucida) and area opaca and showed the presence of more than two $\alpha 1$ chains for each $\alpha 2$ chain. This suggests synthesis of both Type I collagen (con-

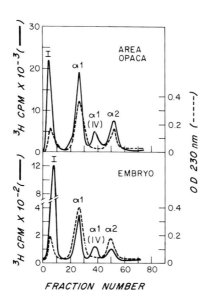

FIG. 16. Primitive streak. CM-cellulose chromatography of newly synthesized, labeled collagen from lathyritic stage 4 chick embryos (area pellucida) and their surrounding area opaca. Stage 4 chick embryos (area pellucida) and their surrounding area opaca were incubated *in situ* (New, 1955) with the addition per milliliter of 64 μg of β-aminopropionitrile and 150 μg of sodium ascorbate. After an hour of preincubation, 2,3,-³H-labeled L-proline was added (200 $\mu Ci/ml$), and incubation was continued for 6 hours. After incubation, the embryos and area opaca were removed, washed free of medium and carefully dissected into two regions: embryonic (area pellucida) and area opaca. These two regions were extracted separately in 1 M NaCl (pH 7.0) for 3 days at 4°C. Extracts were dialyzed against 0.03 M sodium acetate buffer, pH 4.8 in 1.3 M urea and incubated at 50°C for 30 minutes to thermally denature tropocollagen to component α chains. Chromatography was achieved using 0.9 × 10 cm columns of CM-cellulose at 42°C previously equilibrated with starting buffer (0.03 M sodium acetate buffer, pH 4.8, in 1.3 M urea). Collagen α chains were eluted with a linear salt gradient of 125 ml of the above starting buffer and 125 ml of limiting buffer (starting buffer plus 0.1 M NaCl). The position of $\alpha 1$ and $\alpha 2$ chains was determined by measuring the optical density at 230 nm of 25 mg of lathyritic chick skin carrier collagen cochromatographed with the labeled extract. The elution position of $\alpha 1$, $\alpha 2$, and $\alpha 1$ (IV) (from embryonic chick lens collagen) standards are so noted. As is true for all CM-cellulose chromatographs presented in this discussion, recovery of labeled proteins from CM-cellulose was greater than 95%. These two CM-cellulose chromatographs show that these early embryos and their surrounding area opaca make significant levels of Type I, Type IV, and some $(\alpha 1)_3$ collagens.

taining one $\alpha2$ chain per two $\alpha1$ chains) and, in addition, an $(\alpha1)_3$ collagen.

The additional peak which elutes between standard $\alpha1$ and $\alpha2$ chains is more prominent in area pellucida (embryo) than area opaca (Fig. 16). This peak elutes in the same position relative to standard $\alpha1$ and $\alpha2$ chains, as do authentic $\alpha1(IV)$ chains made by embryonic chick lens epithelium). Thus early chick embryos probably make the basal lamina-type collagen $[\alpha1(IV)]_3$. These putative $\alpha1(IV)$ chains have a molecular weight of 115,000 (Fig. 17), and about 74% of the proline residues are hydroxylated in the third and fourth positions (Tables XIII and XIV).

TABLE XIII

PROLINE HYDROXYLATION

Location	Hydroxy-proline	Proline	Percent hydroxylation
Area opaca			
$\alpha1$	6023	6320	48.9
$\alpha2$	2079	2788	43.2
$\alpha1(IV)$	1895	642	73.9
Area pellucida			
$\alpha1$	6331	6980	47.6
$\alpha2$	222	267	48.4
$\alpha1(IV)$	161	58	74.1

TABLE XIV

HYDROXYPROLINE ISOMERS

Location	HyP^a	HyP^{3a}	% HyP^3
Area opaca			
$\alpha1$	5971	52	1.5
$\alpha2$	1859	36	1.9
$\alpha1(IV)$	1354	441	24.6
Area pellucida			
$\alpha1(IV)$	115	46	28.6

^{a} HyP = 4-hydroxyproline; HyP^3 = 3-hydroxyproline.

The detection of a significant level of 3-hydroxyproline is consistent with the identification of these chains as $\alpha1(IV)$ (Kefalides, 1971, 1972). Approximately 5% of total collagen synthesis reflects Type IV collagen. Unfortunately, insufficient amounts of these labeled chains were present to allow of comparing their cyanogen bromide peptides with those of unequivocal α1(IV) chains.

Attempts were made to answer a number of fundamental questions posed by the synthesis of α1 and α2 chains. Did the presence of α2 chains indicate synthesis of Type I collagen similar to that of older tissues? Did the synthesis of more than two α1 chains per α2 chain represent synthesis of some Type II collagen (even though the embryos were clearly prechondrogenic), Type III collagen, or possibly some unknown form of (α1)₃ collagen? It was necessary to use labeled material synthesized by the area opaca since insufficient labeled α1 chains were obtainable from the area pellucida.

Labeled material that eluted with standard α1 and α2 chains was the same size as normal α chains (MW 95,000) and had 44–48% of proline hydroxylated, but only in the fourth position (Fig. 17 and Tables XIII and XIV).

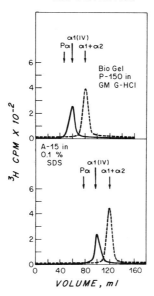

GEL FILTRATION

FIG. 17. The size of labeled collagen chains isolated from the CM-cellulose chromatograph of extracts of area opaca from stage 4 embryos (Fig. 16) was measured by chromatography on molecular sieve columns in denaturing solvents. Labeled α chains were chromatographed on 0.9 × 100 cm. columns of Bio-Gel P-150 (50–100 mesh) in 6 M guanidine-HCl, pH 8.0, or Bio-Gel A-1.5 (50–100 mesh) in 0.1% sodium dodecyl sulfate (SDS)-0.1 M sodium phosphate buffer, pH 7.0, at 8 ml per hour. The elution position of α1, α2, α1(IV), and procollagen (Pα) chains was determined by cochromatography of proline-^{14}C labeled standards whose molecular weights had been calibrated against those of standard proteins as described by Fish et al.

When labeled α1 chains were chromatographed on DEAE-cellulose, they eluted only with authentic carrier α1(I) chains, suggesting the absence of α1(II) chains, hence the absence of detectable Type II collagen synthesis (Fig. 18). Thus at the time of primitive streak formation, the

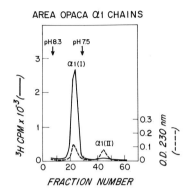

AREA OPACA α1 CHAINS

FIG. 18. Labeled α1 chains synthesized by the area opaca (beginning with stage 4 embryos) and isolated by CM-cellulose chromatography (Fig. 16) were chromatographed on DEAE-cellulose at 42°C according to the procedure of Trelstad *et al.* (1972), except for the addition of 1.3 M urea to all solutions. The α1 chains were dialyzed against 3% acetic acid, freeze-dried, and dialyzed again against 0.004 M Tris-HCl, pH 9.7 in 1.3 M urea before application on a 0.9 × 5 cm DE52 cellulose (Whatman) column at 42°C. The eluting buffers consisted of the following: (a) starting buffer, 0.004 Tris-HCl, pH 9.7 in 1.3 M urea, (b) first-step change, 0.004 M Tris-HCl, pH 8.3, in 1.3 M ura which eluted α1(I) and (c) second-step change, 0.004 M Tris-HCl, pH 7.5, in 1.3 M urea to elute α1(II). The position of α1(I) and α1(II) was determined by optical density at 230 nm using standards. Note that no synthesized α1(II) chains were observed.

area opaca, and quite probably also the area pellucida, make collagen chains that are, by several criteria, similar to those of Type I and Type III collagen of more mature chick tissues. Attempts to examine cyanogen bromide peptides were not entirely successful because of the relatively small amount of material.

2. *Collagen Synthesis by Stage 8+ to 10+ Chick Embryos*

After labeling (in New culture), hearts were removed, embryos were cut transversely into regions that contained, respectively, head, anterior (fore) somites, middle somites, posterior somites, and presomite region (sinus rhomboidalis and primitive streak), and collagen was extracted from pooled samples of each region. All regions contained labeled proteins that coeluted with authentic α1 and α2 chains (Fig. 19). Pooled fractions coeluting with authentic α1 and α2 chains migrate with MW 95,000 α chains on SDS–acrylamide gel and had 45–49% of their labeled proline

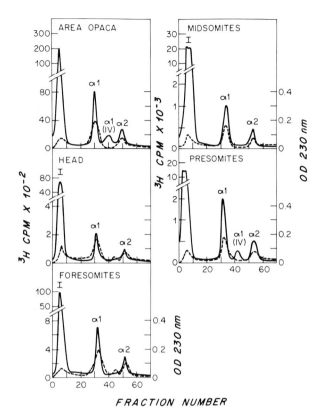

FRACTION NUMBER

FIG. 19. Collagen synthesis by different regions of chick embryos from stage 8+ to 11+ was studied *in situ* as described in Fig. 16 for stage 4 embryos. After a 6-hour incubation in proline-^{3}H, embryos were carefully dissected into different regions and extracted separately with 1 M NaCl. Extracts of labeled proteins were thermally denatured and analyzed by CM-cellulose chromatography at 42°C as described in Fig. 16. The elution position of $\alpha1$ and $\alpha2$ chains was indicated by the cochromatography of lathyritic chick skin collagen as monitored by the optical density at 230 nm (dashed lines). The elution position of $\alpha1(IV)$ chains was determined by chromatography of embryonic chick lens α chains. The elution of radioactive proteins is indicated by a solid line. As only slightly more than two $\alpha1$ chains were synthesized per $\alpha2$ chain, Type I collagen appears to be the major type of collagen made by these young embryonic regions.

hydroxylated (Table XV). The ratio of $\alpha1$ and $\alpha2$ was very close to 2:1, which would be expected if only Type 1 collagen were made. Although small, the excess synthesis of $\alpha1$ chains relative to $\alpha2$ chains (2.5 for head region, 2.4 for anterior somite region, and 2.70 for the presomite region) is sufficiently greater than 2:1 to suggest the synthesis of a low level ($<10\%$ total collagen synthesis) of synthesis of an $(\alpha1)_3$ collagen.

FRANCIS J. MANASEK

TABLE XV

PROLINE HYDROXYLATION

Location	Hydroxyproline	Proline	% Hydroxyproline
Head			
α1	748	851	46.9
α2	275	344	44.5
Foresomites			
α1	827	939	46.8
α2	291	362	44.9
Midsomites			
α1	803	1017	45.1
α2	390	553	46.3
Presomites			
α1	1631	1965	47.0
α2	583	207	46.1
α1(IV)	645	741	73.5
Heart			
α1	405	393	49.2
α2	191	186	49.3
Area opaca			
α1	725	831	46.6
α2	390	338	46.5
α1(IV)	181	69	72.5

Collagen synthesized by developing hearts (of 6–11 somite embryos) is seemingly Type I, and no suggestion of other types was found. A correlative biochemical and morphological study (Johnson et al., 1974) showed that crossbanded collagen becomes detectable in the cardiac matrix during this time (about 9 somites). This study also confirmed earlier observations (Manasek, 1968) that the myocardium develops a basal lamina during this period, yet surprisingly no Type IV α chains were detectable in the heart. This is in distinct contrast to the detection of a peak that eluted between α1 and α2 chains in the position expected for α1(IV) chains in the presomite (sinus rhomboidalis and primitive streak) portion of the same embryos.

The intact embryos we used in these studies seemingly did not synthesize the unique collagen that is made in culture by trypsinized neural tubes isolated from stage 12 to 15 embryos (16 to ca 25 somites; 45–55 hours of incubation) (Trelstad et al., 1973) or the apparent Type II collagen made by similarly treated notochords from 2.5-day-old (stage 17; 30 somites) embryos (Linsenmayer et al., 1937a). This may simply reflect the fact that we are using younger embryos. On the other hand, neural tube and/or notochord may well modulate the type of collagen synthesized *in vitro* as a result of culture conditions. Collagen synthesized by these tissues in culture may also represent a regeneration molecule made only during the *in vitro* repair process. Careful ultrastructural studies have shown that trypsinization removes basal laminae that are already associated with neural tube (Cohen and Hay, 1971) and notochord (Carlson, 1973a,b) permitting direct contact between the cell basal plasmalemmas and the artificial environment of the culture medium. In both tissues a basal lamina is regenerated in culture (Cohen and Hay, 1971; Carlson and Evans, 1973) within the first two days, and it is during this period of regeneration that label is introduced (Trelstad *et al.*, 1973; Linsenmayer *et al.*, 1973a).

C. DEVELOPMENTAL SIGNIFICANCE

It is perhaps not premature to make some generalizations about embryonic matrix prior to the appearance of true connective tissues. Clearly, these very early embryonic extracellular matrices are dynamic and biochemically heterogeneous. Neither collagen, chondroitin sulfate, nor hyaluronate are unique to older, more defined, and better understood matrices but appear to be synthesized at all stages examined. Although primitive streak area opaca makes Type III collagen and this region, along with slightly older presomite, areas makes Type IV collagen, the predominant species appears to be Type I. The absence of Type II collagen synthesis in these preconnective tissue stage embryos is consistent with the notion that this collagen truly represents the expression of the chondrogenic phenotype.

The level of collagen synthesis in these early embryonic tissues is far lower than that observed in mature connective tissues. About 0.2% of proline labeled proteins of primitive streak embryos and 5–10% of proline-labeled proteins made by chick tissues from state 8+ to 10+ represents collagen synthesis. Proline represents 20% of collagen (see Table I) and is present in very low levels in most other proteins. Consequently, this suggests that collagen is a minor component of these early embryonic extracellular matrices.

The similarity of the early embryonic Types I, III, and IV with their more mature counterparts, suggests either a developmental continuity of types of collagen, or the inability of our analysis to detect subtle heterogeneities. One should, however, be cautious in equating these early embryonic matrices with more mature matrices on the basis of homologous collagenous and glycosaminoglycan polysaccharide components. Some evidence does exist suggesting developmental changes in the size (Palmoski and Goetinck, 1972) and perhaps in the amino acid composition of the protein of proteochondroitin sulfate. Also, it is becoming more evi-

dent that collagens can be linked intimately to noncollagenous glycoprotein and phosphoproteins in certain tissues, by bonds whose establishment
is inhibited by experimental lathryrism. Thus, there are at least two
possible differences between early embryonic and more mature matrices
that are not all explored by the preceding data and discussion.

The regional differences in collagen synthesis described in the previous
section do not necessarily represent compositional differences. As such,
attempts to implicate collagens in developmental processes by trying to
discern correlations between synthesis and morphogenetic events is, at
this time, fruitless. Furthermore, in these studies as in all analytical
studies, failure to detect either presence or synthesis does not necessarily
mean absence. Amounts of material below the limit of resolution, but
still biologically active, may be present.

Although some insight into distribution of glycosaminoglycans can
be gained by means of radioautography, we simply do not know the location of different types of collagen in the normal intact embryo. However,
it can only be exciting that so much biochemical homology does exist
between early embryonic and more mature extracellular matrices in spite
of their differences in morphological appearance.

The development of both glycosaminoglycan core protein and glycoproteins was ignored. This omission is based on ignorance, not on bias.
Glycoproteins are certainly being synthesized during early as well as late
embryonic development. In our laboratory we have preliminary data
demonstrating, by means of fucose-^{3}H incorporation, extensive deposition
of extracellular glycoprotein between stages 4 through 12 (primitive
streak to 16 somites). Somite sclerotome regions are particularly rich in
labeled glycoproteins (Fig. 20) which are also synthesized by neural tube
and notochord (Manasek, unpublished observations). It is clear from
radioautographic studies that these glycoproteins are not entirely membrane-associated but represent a true constituent of the extracellular
compartment. They are electrophoretically heterogeneous as determined
by gel electrophoresis and are sensitive to Pronase digestion (Manasek,
unpublished observations). Thus, glycoproteins are present, yet we know
nothing about their precise composition or possible importance in such
events as sclerotome chondrogenesis.

VI. Changing Matrix Synthesis in Some Developing Embryonic
Chick Connective Tissues

Studies of macromolecules during embryonic chick sclerotome chondrogenesis and corneal development have provided some insight into the
synthesis of different types of glycosaminoglycan polysaccharide (Abbott
et al., 1972; Conrad, 1970; Ellison and Lash, 1971; Franco-Browder *et*

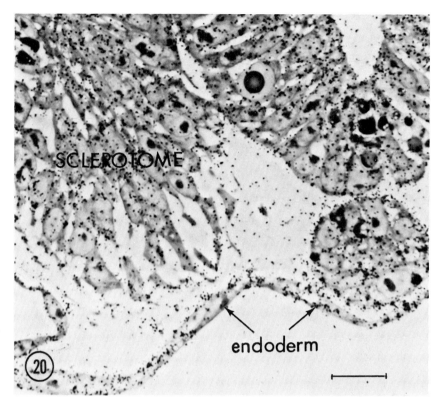

Fig. 20. Despite the fact that virtually nothing is known about the structure and composition of extracellular glycoproteins during embryonic development, these molecules are widely distributed in embryos. In this example of a radioautograph of a section of an 11-somite chick embryo incubated with fucose-³H, extracellular label surrounds neural tube and notochord and is associated with sclerotome. This major class of compounds has been neglected although these compounds may quite possibly be instrumental in embryonic tissue interactions. Calibration equals 10 μm.

al., 1963; Lash, 1968; Marzullo and Lash, 1970; Meier and Hay, 1973; Toole, 1972; Toole and Trelstad, 1971). Most of these studies measured synthesis using labeled precursors, and it is difficult to interpret them quantitatively in terms of composition (see Section III, B). The compositional studies of axial glycosaminoglycans (Kvist and Finnegan, 1970) represent an effort to circumvent this problem. Interestingly, their data are in apparent conflict with studies of synthesis. Also, many of these studies used tissue labeled *in vitro* and did not establish analogy to *in vivo* synthetic patterns. In fact, synthesis of glycosaminoglycan polysaccharide in the embryonic chick cornea *in vitro* has been shown in two instances to differ quantitatively and qualitatively from its counterpart *in ovo* (Conrad, 1970; compare also Tables 1–3 in Toole and Trelstad, 1971). The size and synthetic activities of many of these tissues make analysis of synthesis of other matrix molecules, such as collagen and glycosaminoglycan core protein, more difficult, and such studies have not yet been done.

A. CHANGING GLYCOSAMINOGLYCAN SYNTHESIS DURING EMBRYONIC CHICK CHONDROGENESIS

The appearance of cartilage in young chick embryos has been one of the most widely studied events of early differentiation. The ability to define morphologically an apparent cartilaginous tissue has led to many attempts to excise the tissue and analyze its development in culture using metachromasia and/or $^{35}SO_4{}^{2-}$ incorporation as indices of normal chondrogenesis (for discussion, see Searls, 1973a,b). However, many early embryonic chick and anuran tissues that are unquestionably nonchondrogenic, make chondroitin sulfates 4 and 6, an observation suggesting that these sulfated glycosaminoglycans are a general component of many different early embryonic extracellular matrices (Johnston and Comar, 1957; Kosher and Searls, 1973; Manasek *et al.*, 1973). Hence, attempts to score chondrogenesis simply by $^{35}SO_4{}^{2-}$ incorporation or metachromasia are inadequate. Moreover, attempts to quantitate the amount of sulfated glycosaminoglycans synthesized ("more" is generally considered an indication of "differentiation") by measurement of incorporated ^{35}S alone is subject to the problems discussed in Section III, B.

The predominant glycosaminoglycan of embryonic cartilage contains chondroitin sulfates 4 and 6 as its polysaccharide component, gradually shifting to only chondroitin sulfate 6 with maturation. Keratan sulfate appears in mature cartilage, usually as a minor component. Chondroitin may also be a minor component. Generally, it is assumed that cartilage does not contain dermatan sulfate (chondroitin sulfate B), heparin, heparan sulfate, and hyaluronate (Kaplan and Meyer, 1959; Mathews and Glagov, 1966; Davidson and Small, 1963; Robinson and Dorfman, 1969).

1. Chondroitin Sulfates during Cartilage Development

Examination of sulfated glycosaminoglycan synthesis by two different embryonic chick cartilages (keel and articular) *in vivo* and *in vitro* show the expected developmental transformation from mixed synthesis of chondroitin sulfates 4 and 6 to synthesis of predominantly chondroitin sulfate 6 (Fig. 21). Seemingly, analysis of the relative proportion of chondroitin sulfates 4 to 6 synthesized could provide an extremely sensitive criterion against which to evaluate the analogy of *in vitro* chondrogenesis to the

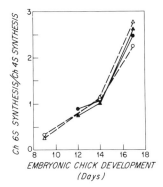

FIG. 21. Chondroitin sulfate synthesis was analyzed during the development of embryonic chick keel (*in ovo*, ●——●; *in vitro*, ○- - -○) and proximal tibia (*in ovo*, ▲——▲; *in vitro*, △---△) cartilages by incorporation of $^{35}SO_4^{2-}$ for 12 hours *in ovo* or *in vitro*. Cartilages were incubated *in vitro* in F-10 medium plus 10% fetal calf serum and 150 μg of sodium ascorbate per milliliter. After an hour of preincubation, $^{35}SO_4^{2-}$ was added at 200 μCi/ml. Labeled cartilages were digested with papain to remove proteins (Manasek, *et al.*, 1973) then digested with chondroitinase ABC (Yamagata *et al.*, 1968), and ΔDi 4S and ΔDi 6S dissaccharides were analyzed according to the procedure of Robinson and Dorfman (1969). The relative synthesis of ΔDi 4S and ΔDi 6S dissaccharide represented the relative synthesis of chondroitin 4-sulfate (Ch 4S) and chondroitin 6-sulfate (Ch 6S).

normal *in ovo* chondrogenesis for any particular cartilage at any embryonic age studied.

Chondroitin sulfate produced by developing cartilage *in situ* is predominantly fully sulfated (Figs. 22 and 23). This suggests that if synthesis of undersulfated chondroitin sulfate is predominant in cultured chondrocytes, the culture may not be an analogue of matrix synthesis *in situ*.

2. Keratan Sulfate Synthesis

Vertebral cartilage provides yet another variation on the basic theme, making significant quantities (20%) of a $^{35}SO_4^{2-}$ labeled glycosaminoglycan that coelectrophoreses with fully sulfated chondroitin sulfate but is resistant to testicular hyaluronidase digestion. The material was identified as keratin sulfate on the basis of its insensitivity to chondroitinase ABC digestion (dermatan sulfate is sensitive) and mild nitrous acid hydrolysis (heparin and heparan sulfate are sensitive, see Table XVI). Vertebral cartilage made keratan sulfate from at least 12 to 18 days of embryonic chick development. Schulman and Meyer (1968, 1970) also found a low level of keratan sulfate synthesis by 10-day embryonic chick chondrocytes *in vitro*, but since analogy of their culture system to normal, *in situ*, chondrocytes was not established, they could not exclude the pos-

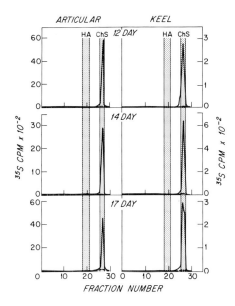

Fig. 22. Embryonic chick keel and articular cartilages labeled for 12 hours *in ovo* with $^{35}SO_4^{2-}$ were digested with papain and glycosaminoglycan polysaccharides separated by electrophoresis on cellulose acetate strips (Manasek *et al.*, 1973). Chondroitin sulfates were distinguished from other sulfated glycosaminoglycan polysaccharides by their susceptibility to testicular hyaluronidase. Labeled glycosaminoglycan polysaccharides in papain digests are represented by a solid line, and those resistant to testicular hyaluronidase are shown by a dashed line. The migration of standard hyaluronate is represented by HA and the migration of chondroitin sulfates 4 and 6 by ChS. Similar electrophorograms, showing synthesis of only fully sulfated chondroitin sulfates 4 and 6, were obtained from these embryonic chick cartilages labeled with $^{35}SO_4^{2-}$ *in vitro* under conditions described in Fig. 21.

TABLE XVI

Stability of Vertebral Cartilage Sulfated Glycosaminoglycans[a]

Age	Total cpm	Testicular hyaluronidase resistant cpm	Chondroitinase ABC resistant cpm	Nitrous acid resistant
12 Days	4617	1015	1043	1034
14 Days	8346	1323	1289	1392
18 Days	7851	1480	1454	1126

[a] Equal aliquots were treated with testicular hyaluronidase, chondroitinase ABC, or nitrous acid or were left as controls. Samples were then precipitated in 1% cetyl pyridinium chloride with 1 mg of carrier chondroitin sulfates 4 and 6, and the precipitate was counted by liquid scintillation.

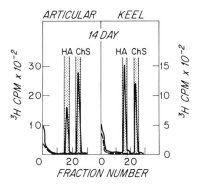

FIG. 23. Keel and articular cartilage were labeled with acetate-³H *in ovo* for 12 hours, and the labeled glycosaminoglycan polysaccharides were analyzed electrophoretically as described in Fig. 21. The migration of standard hyaluronate is indicated by HA, and the migration of standard chondroitin sulfates 4 and 6 is indicated by ChS. Labeled glycosaminoglycans of papain digests are shown by a solid line, and those resistant to testicular hyaluronidase by a dashed line. Analysis of the labeled monosaccharide subunits showed labeled D-glucuronate, *N*-acetyl-D-glucosamine labeled in the *N*-acetyl group and hexose carbon backbone, and *N*-acetyl-D-galactosamine labeled only in the *N*-acetyl group. The recovery of labeled *N*-acetyl-D-glucosamine demonstrates that the testicular hyaluronidase-sensitive labeled material comigrating with standard hyaluronate contains significant quantities of hyaluronate. Therefore hyaluronate is synthesized *normally* by these two embryonic chick cartilages.

sibility that keratan sulfate synthesis was an adaptation to culture condition. Similarly, a number of workers have detected synthesis of an unidentified polysaccharide by cultured chondrocytes. Glick and Stockdale (1964) and Nameroff and Holtzer (1967) working with 10-day embryonic chick vertebral chondrocytes *in vitro* determined that this sulfated material contained D-glucosamine or *N*-acetyl-D-glucosamine. In all likelihood this material is keratan sulfate.

3. *Hyaluronate Synthesis*

Hyaluronate is a normal matrix component of differentiated cartilage, and its synthesis is compatible with both expression and retention of the chondrogenic phenotype. Use of acetate-³H *in ovo* and of acetate-³H, acetate-¹⁴C, D-glucosamine-6-³H, *in vitro* showed that embryonic chick keel and articular cartilage made an unsulfated glycosaminoglycan with the electrophoretic mobility for hyaluronate (for representative incorporation patterns, see Figs. 23–25). It was sensitive to testicular hyaluronidase and was solubilized from a CPC-cellulose column by the same salt concentration as hyaluronate (0.5 *M* NaCl). It was further identified as hyaluronate by detection of the presence of incorporated, labeled

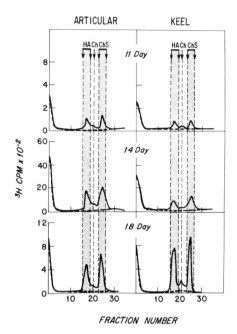

FIG. 24. Keel and articular cartilages isolated from 11-, 14-, and 18-day chick embryos were labeled with acetate-³H *in vitro* (200 μCi/ml) for 12 hours under conditions described in Fig. 21. Labeled glycosaminoglycan polysaccharides of papain digests (solid line) and those resistant to testicular hyaluronidase (dashed line) were analyzed electrophoretically as described in Fig. 22. The migration of standard hyaluronate is indicated by HA, and chondroitin sulfates 4 and 6 by ChS. Analysis of labeled monosaccharides from glycosaminoglycan polysaccharides showed significant labeling of N-acetyl-ᴅ-glucosamine, which indicated that a significant portion of the testicular hyaluronidase-sensitive, acetate-labeled material comigrating with standard hyaluronate is actually hyaluronate. As acetate-¹⁴C labeled glycosaminoglycan polysaccharides gave the same results, hyaluronate was not labeled by tritium exchange from acetate-³H. Embryonic chick keel and articular cartilages synthesize hyaluronate both *in ovo* and *in vitro*.

N-acetylglucosamine following acid hydrolysis of cartilage incubated with labeled acetate or glucosamine.

The finding that hyaluronate synthesis did represent the normal expression of the chondrogenic phenotype is particularly interesting in light of the current concept of structure of the proteochondroitin sulfate *aggregate*, which involves hyaluronate in its structure. The basic structural unit of proteochondroitin sulfate is the proteochondroitin subunit, composed of core protein covalently linked to chondroitin sulfate (and also to keratan sulfate in mature cartilage). The proteochondroitin sulfate subunits interact noncovalently with a glycoprotein–hyaluronate back-

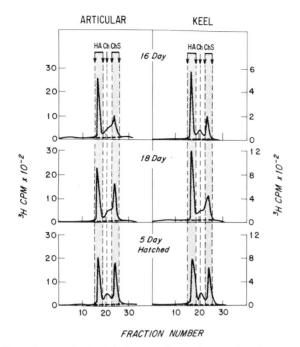

FIG. 25. The glucosamine-³H-labeled cartilage glycosaminoglycans made by 16- and 18-day chick embryos and 5-day-old chicks were analyzed as in Fig. 22. As these glucosamine-³H-labeled glycosaminoglycan polysaccharides contain labeled *N*-acetyl-D-glucosamine and *N*-acetyl-D-galactosamine, glucosamine-³H is labeling both hyaluronate and chondroitin sulfates. Ch represents the leading edge of the chondroitin standard. Under these conditions, chondroitin is not entirely separable from hyaluronate.

bone to form the proteochondroitin sulfate aggregate (Gregory, 1973; Rosenberg, 1973). Only a low level of hyaluronate (in the order of several percent composition) is needed to permit assembly of the proteoglycan aggregate (Hardingham and Muir, 1972).

4. Incorporation of Label into Glycosaminoglycans

The relative labeling of the material coelectrophoresing with hyaluronate and fully sulfated chondroitin sulfates 4 and 6 was examined after incubation with acetate-³H *in ovo* or *in vitro* and D-glucosamine-³H *in vitro;* it shows a relatively large amount of label appearing in hyaluronate (compare Figs. 23, 24, and 25). This probably does not represent the actual relative level of synthesis of hyaluronate, but rather preferential incorporation of labeled precursor as a result of two phenomena: (1) acetate can label the monosaccharide subunits of glycosaminoglycan in more than one position (see Fig. 3); and (2) the specific activities at which these labeled precursors label the three different monosaccharides (glucuronate and the 2 N-acetylhexosamines) are not equal, but are a function of both the relative rates of incorporation of the labeled precursor employed as well as the position at which the labeled precursor is incorporated (see Section III, B).

The simplest example is that of D-glucosamine-^{3}H incorporation. In articular and keel cartilage prior to 14 days of embryonic chick development, D-glucosamine-^{3}H is incorporated principally into hyaluronate (as N-acetyl-D-glucosamine). After 14 days of development, it still appears in hyaluronate (as N-acetyl-D-glucosamine) but also significantly in chondroitin sulfates as N-acetylgalactosamine. However, investigation of soluble, unincorporated pools prior to 14 days of embryonic development showed significant epimerization of D-glucosamine-^{3}H-labeled UDP-N-acetyl-D-glucosamine to UDP-N-acetyl-D-galactosamine. Similarly, acetate-^{3}H *in ovo* or *in vitro* predominantly labels incorporated N-acetyl-D-glucosamine as compared to N-acetyl-D-galactosamine, although both unincorporated UDP-N-acetyl-D-glucosamine and UDP-N-acetyl-D-galactosamine are labeled.

These observations suggest that although the UDP-N-acetylglucosamine–UDP-N-acetyl-D-galactosamine epimerase does work *in ovo*, there may be a large endogenous UDP-N-acetyl-D-galactosamine pool that makes the specific activity of incorporated labeled UDP-N-acetyl-D-galactosamine low enough to make difficult its detection as part of chondroitin sulfate prior to 14 days of embryonic development for chick keel or articular cartilage.

These observations highlight the pitfalls of making qualitative or quantitative evaluation of glycosaminoglycan synthesis employing labeled precursors. Unequal pool-specific activities of UPD-N-acetylglucosamine and UDP-N-acetylgalactosamine labeled by any of a variety of labeled precursors result in quantitatively erroneous measurements of synthesis of chondroitin sulfates and hyaluronate. It is not difficult to envisage that differences of 10- to 20-fold in the pool specific activities of these two UDP-N-acetylhexosamines would also produce qualitatively erroneous results in which synthesis of a glycosaminoglycan cannot be detected.

Throughout these studies of matrix macromolecule synthesis most labeling was done *in vitro* because of technical problems presented by label utilization and use of lathryogens *in ovo*. Possible cellular changes in response to medium were obviated by using intact tissue in which cells were surrounded by their normal extracellular matrix. There are a number of lines of evidence indicating that the culture conditions employed in these studies permit normal development and synthesis. Early embryos grown in New (1955) cultures undergo normal morphogenesis on a normal time scale. Comparison of glycosaminoglycan polysaccharide synthesis by keel in organ culture to keel *in ovo* (see Fig. 21 compare Figs. 23 and 24) shows that the tissue maintains its normal synthetic activities *in vitro*.

Since these studies examined synthesis, they are subject to the qualifications discussed in Section III. Unfortunately, there are no direct compositional analyses of glycosaminoglycan polysaccharides to show the relationship between synthetic and compositional changes. Changes in relative content of chondroitin 4- and 6-sulfates have been described for a number of developing cartilages (Kaplan and Meyer, 1959; Davidson and Small, 1963; Mathews and Glagov, 1966; Robinson and Dorfman, 1969) and apparently reflect the synthetic changes that have been discussed.

B. INTERACTION BETWEEN MATRIX MACROMOLECULES

Until now, we have treated different matrix macromolecules separately and as though they did not interact as part of the matrix. Such an approach may give an erroneously simple picture of extracellular matrix.

In cartilage matrix, where it has been studied, it has been shown that collagen and glycosaminoglycans can interact both covalently and noncovalently. This is an important observation, since throughout early development collagen and chondroitin sulfate are ubiquitous. If interactions between these molecules are universal, then clearly matrix properties are more than simple additives of individual component properties.

Most glycosaminoglycan–collagen interaction is noncovalent since the large part of the glycosaminoglycan content of cartilage can be extracted relatively free of collagen by the use of strong denaturing agents such as $CaCl_2$, LiCl, $MgCl_2$, and guanidine-HCl (Rosenberg and Schubert, 1967; Sadjera and Hascall, 1969; Hascall and Sadjera, 1970; Gregory, 1973; Rosenberg, 1973). Data in support of the existence of noncovalent interactions have been obtained *in vitro*. Addition of glycosaminoglycans interferes with tropocollagen fibrillogenesis (Toole and Lowther, 1968; Toole, 1969; Lowther et al., 1970) and glycosaminoglycan binds to insoluble collagen (Mathews, 1970; ÖBrink, 1970). At physiological ionic strength there appears to be weak electrostatic as well as steric bonding between collagen and glycosaminoglycans. Both the protein and polysaccharide glycosaminoglycan components interact with collagen in a manner dependent upon both the size and charge:mass ratio of the glycosaminoglycans. However, removal of the collagen telopeptides (i.e., nonhelical regions) eliminates, or at least drastically diminishes, the interaction (Lowther et al., 1970). Parenthetically, it should be appreciated that these in vitro measures of interaction have used Type I collagen. Since Type II collagen is the predominant collagen of mature cartilage (Miller, 1971a,b,c), it would be most informative to examine the nature of glycosaminoglycan interaction with Type II collagen.

Similar interactions may exist in renal glomerular basal laminae and lens capsule between Type IV collagen and glycoproteins (Kefalides, 1970; Spiro, 1970a,b); in dentine, between Type I and Type III collagen and glycoprotein and phosphoprotein (Volpin and Veis, 1971, 1973), and in bone between Type I collagen, glycoproteins, and phosphoproteins (Spector and Glimcher, 1972).

On the basis of these observations, it is predictable that such interactions are general and involve matrix macromolecules throughout development. The intimate association between fibrillar collagen and ruthenium red-positive material (Fig. 9) may represent such interactions. The possibility that glycoproteins are involved is furthered by findings that the macromolecules are widespread throughout developing matrices (see, for example, Fig. 21).

C. CONCLUDING COMMENTS

Emphasis has been placed on descriptive studies of some molecular characteristics of extracellular matrix and of temporal correlations with other developmental events. In this manner, some aspects of cellular environments during embryonic development have been explored. It should be obvious that although some matrix components have been defined, we cannot yet describe quantitatively the total macromolecular composition of any specific matrix during development.

By concentrating on early stages of embryonic development (except for studies of chondrogenesis), an attempt has been made to elucidate matrix synthesis at a time when the embryo is still histologically simple, yet when major interactions are occurring.

Chronological changes in macromolecules differ among different matrices, but there is no evidence that each different developing tissue synthesizes unique embryonic variants of collagen or glycosaminoglycan polysaccharide. For example, embryonic cartilages that are transient, later to be replaced by bone, synthesize collagen similar to the collagen found in mature cartilage (Linsenmayer et al., 1973b).

No ready distinction can be made between matrix molecules found in primitive streak embryos and those found in older embryonic and mature tissues. The ubiquity of many of these molecules throughout such a range in development and tissue type suggests that they, by themselves, do not have unique determinative effects. We do not know whether other macromolecular components, such as the largely undescribed glycoproteins or the glycosaminoglycan core protein, normally have, by themselves, unique determinative effects. Alternatively, all these components may well be significant only in terms of their roles in an integrated matrix. This is consistent with the observations that suggest a great deal of quantitative variation in synthesis of similar glycosaminoglycan polysaccharides and collagen among vastly different tissues and ages. At the present time one of the greatest hindrances to understanding embryonic extracellular matrix function is the lack of descriptive studies of the molecular content of *normal* extracellular matrices. Studies of *synthesis* are more easily done, and there is an unfortunate tendency to equate synthesis (or simply incorporation of labeled precursor) with content.

However ill-defined developing matrix is at the present time, it is clear that changes in matrix molecule synthesis are rapid, as may be attendant compositional changes. Cellular environments are not static. The mechanisms regulating these changes, and their effects on development, are largely unknown, but it is almost certain that a major key to embryonic development lies in the *milieu interieur embryonique*.

ACKNOWLEDGMENT

I thank Dr. Marijke Holtrop, who kindly provided Fig. 6. The assistance of Ms. M. Reid and Ms. Joan Lacktis is gratefully acknowledged. The original work reported in this paper was supported by HL 10436 and HL 13831 and by the Louis Block Fund, The University of Chicago. A portion of this work was done while the author was a recipient of a Research Career Development Award (HL 50308).

REFERENCES

Abbott, J., Mayne, E., and Holtzer, H. (1972). *Develop. Biol.* **28**, 430–442.
Altgelt, K., Hodge, A. J., and Schmitt, F. O. (1961). *Proc. Nat. Acad. Sci. U.S.* **47**, 1914–1924.
Amprino, R. (1955). *Acta Anat.* **24**, 121–163.
Antonopoulos, C. A., Gardell, S., Szirmai, J. A., and DeTyssonsk, E. R. (1964). *Biochim. Biophys. Acta* **83**, 1–19.
Bailey, A. J. (1968). *Compr. Biochem.* **26B**, 297–423.
Balazs, E. A. (1958). *Fed. Proc., Fed. Amer. Soc. Exp. Biol.* **17**, 1086–1092.
Barnes, M. J., Constable, B. J., Morton, L. F., and Kodicek, E. (1973). *Biochem. J.* **132**, 113–115.
Bennett, H. S. (1963). *J. Histochem. Cytochem.* **11**, 14–23.
Bernfield, M. R., and Banerjee, S. D. (1972). *J. Cell Biol.* **52**, 664–673.
Bernfield, M. R., and Wessells, N. K. (1970). *Develop. Biol. Suppl.* **4**, 195–249.
Bernfield, M. R., Banerjee, S. D., and Cohn, R. H. (1972). *J. Cell Biol.* **52**, 674–689.
Bernfield, M. R., Cohn, R. H., and Banerjee, S. D. (1973). *Amer. Zool.* **13**, 1067–1083.
Bornstein, P., Kang, A. H., and K. A. (1966). *Biochemistry* **5**, 3803–3812.
Boström, H., and Aqvist, S. (1952). *Acta Chem. Scand.* **6**, 1557–1559.

Burge, R. E., and Hynes, R. B. (1959). *J. Mol. Biol.* 1, 155–164.
Butler, W. T., Miller, E. J., and Finch, J. E. (1974). *Biochem. Biophys. Res. Commun.* 57, 190–195.
Cannon, W. B. (1929). *Physiol. Rev.* 9, 399–431.
Carlson, E. C. (1973a). *Amer. J. Anat.* 136, 77–90.
Carlson, E. C. (1973b). *J. Ultrastruct. Res.* 42, 287–297.
Carlson, E. C., and Evans, D. K. (1973). *Anat. Rec.* 175, 284(A).
Chung, E., and Miller, E. J. (1974). *Science* 183, 1200–1201.
Cifonelli, J. A. (1968). *Carbohyd. Res.* 8, 233–242.
Cifonelli, J. A. (1970). "Chemistry and Molecular Biology of the Intercellular Matrix" (E. A. Balazs, ed.), Vol. 2, pp. 951–967. Academic Press, New York.
Click, E. M., and Bornstein, P. (1970). *Biochemistry* 9, 4699–4706.
Cohen, A. M., and Hay, E. D. (1971). *Develop. Biol.* 26, 578–605.
Conrad, G. (1970). *Develop. Biol.* 21, 611–635.
Davidson, E. A., and Small, W. (1963). *Biochim. Biophys. Acta* 69, 459–463.
Dische, Z. (1947). *J. Biol. Chem.* 167, 189–198.
Duran-Reynals, F. (1955). *Ann. N.Y. Acad. Sci.* 52, 943–1000.
Dziewiatkowski, D. D. (1958). *Int. Rev. Cytol.* 7, 159–193.
Ellison, M. L., and Lash, J. W. (1971). *Develop. Biol.* 26, 486–496.
Fish, W. W., Mann, K. G., and Tanford, C. (1969). *J. Biol. Chem.* 244, 4989–4994.
Franek, M. D., and Dunstone, J. R. (1967). *J. Biol. Chem.* 242, 3460–3467.
Franco-Browder, S., De Rydt, J., and Dorfman, A. (1963). *Proc. Nat. Acad. Sci. U.S.* 49, 643–647.
François, C. J., and Glimcher, M. J. (1965). *Biochim. Biophys. Acta* 97, 366–369.
François, C. J., and Glimcher, M. J. (1967). *Biochim. Biophys. Acta* 133, 91–96.
Fransson, L. A. (1970). *In* "Chemistry and Molecular Biology of the Intercellular Matrix" (E. A. Balazs, ed.), Vol. 2, pp. 823–842. Academic Press, New York.
Fredrickson, R. G., and Low, F. N. (1971). *Amer. J. Anat.* 130, 347–376.
Furthmayr, H., and Timpl, R. (1971). *Anal. Biochem.* 41, 510–516.
Gallop, P. M., Blumenfeld, O. O., and Seifter, S. (1972). *Annu. Rev. Biochem.* 41, 617–672.
Glick, M. J., and Stockdale, F. (1964). *Biochim. Biophys. Acta* 83, 61–68.
Glimcher, M. J., Brickley, D. M., and Seyer, J. M. (1969). *Biochem. J.* 115, 923–926.
Glimcher, M. J., François, C. J., Richards, L., and Krane, S. M. (1964). *Biochim. Biophys. Acta* 93, 585–602.
Golub, L., Stern, B., Glimcher, M., and Goldhaber, P. (1968). *Proc. Soc. Exp. Biol. Med.* 129, 465–469.
Grant, M. E., and Prockop, D. J. (1972). *N. Engl. J. Med.* 286, 194–199, 242–249, and 291–300.
Green, H., Goldberg, B., Schwartz, M., and Brown, D. D. (1968). *Develop. Biol.* 18, 391–399.
Gregory, J. D. (1973). *Biochem. J.* 133, 383–386.
Greiling, H., Kisters, R., and Stuhlsatz, H. W. (1970). *In* "Chemistry and Molecular Biology of the Intercellular Matrix" (E. A. Balazs, ed.), Vol. 2, pp. 759–762. Academic Press, New York.
Grobstein, C. (1967). *Nat. Cancer Inst., Monogr.* 26, 279–299.
Gross, J. (1958). *J. Exp. Med.* 107, 247–263.
Hardingham, T. E., and Muir, H. (1972). *Biochim. Biophys. Acta* 279, 401–405.
Hascall, V. C., and Sadjera, S. W. (1970). *J. Biol. Chem.* 245, 4920–4930.
Hay, E. D. (1973). *Amer. Zool.* 13, 1085–1107.

Hay, E. D., and Dodson, J. W. (1973). *J. Cell Biol.* **57**, 190–213.
Hay, E. D., and S. Meier (1974). *J. Cell Biol.* **62**, 889–898.
Hirsch, J. G., and Fedorko, M. E. (1968). *J. Cell Biol.* **38**, 615–621.
Hodge, A. J. (1967). In "Treatise on Collagen" (G. N. Ramachandran, ed.), Vol. 1, pp. 186–205. Academic Press, New York.
Horwitz, A. I., and Dorfman, A. (1968). *J. Cell Biol.* **38**, 358–368.
Huet, C., and Herzberg, M. (1973). *J. Ultrastruct. Res.* **42**, 186–199.
Igarashi, S., Kang, A. H., and Gross, J. (1970). *Biochem. Biophys. Res. Commun.* **38**, 697–702.
Immers, J. (1961). *Exp. Cell Res.* **24**, 356–378.
Johnson, R. C., Manasek, F. J., Vinson, W. C., and Seyer, J. M. (1974). *Develop. Biol.* **36**, 252–271.
Johnston, P. M., and Comar, C. L. (1957). *J. Biophys. Biochem. Cytol.* **3**, 231–245.
Kang, A. H., Piez, K. A., and Gross, J. (1969a). *Biochemistry* **8**, 1506–1514.
Kang, A. H., Igarashi, S., and Gross, J. (1969b). *Biochemistry* **8**, 3200–3204.
Kang, A. H., Piez, K. A., and Gross, J. (1969c). *Biochemistry* **8**, 3648–3655.
Kaplan, D., and Meyer, K. (1959). *Nature (London)* **183**, 1267–1268.
Kefalides, N. A. (1970). In "Chemistry and Molecular Biology of the Intercellular Matrix" (E. A. Balazs, ed.), Vol. 1, pp. 535–573. Academic Press, New York.
Kefalides, N. A. (1971). *Biochem. Biophys. Res. Commun.* **45**, 226–234.
Kefalides, N. A. (1972). *Biochem. Biophys. Res. Commun.* **47**, 1151–1158.
Kefalides, N. A. (1973). *Int. Rev. Connect. Tissue Res.* **6**, 63–104.
Klöse, J., and Flickinger, R. A. (1971). *Biochim. Biophys. Acta* **232**, 207–211.
Klotz, I. M., and Darnall, D. W. (1969). *Science* **166**, 126–128.
Kosher, R. A., and Searls, R. L. (1973). *Develop. Biol.* **32**, 50–68.
Kvist, T. N., and Finnegan, C. V. (1970). *J. Exp. Zool.* **175**, 221–240.
Lash, J. W. (1968). *J. Cell. Physiol.* **72**, 35–46.
Layman, D. L., Sokoloff, L., and Miller, E. J. (1972) *Exp. Cell Res.* **73**, 107–112.
Leblond, C. P. (1950). *Amer. J. Anat.* **86**, 1–49.
Lesseps, R. J. (1967). *J. Cell Biol.* **34**, 173–183.
Levenson, G. E. (1969). *Exp. Cell Res.* **55**, 433–435.
Lindahl, U. (1970). In "Chemistry and Molecular Biology of the Intercellular Matrix" (E. A. Balazs, ed.), Vol. 2, pp. 943–960. Academic Press, New York.
Linker, A., Hoffman, P., Meyer, K., Sampson, P., and Korn, E. D. (1960). *J. Biol. Chem.* **235**, 3061–3065.
Linsenmayer, T. F., Trelstad, R. L., and Gross, J. (1973a). *Biochem. Biophys. Res. Commun.* **53**, 39–45.
Linsenmayer, T. F., Trelstad, R. L., Toole, B. P., and Gross, J. (1973b). *Biochem. Biophys. Res. Commun.* **52**, 870–876.
Low, F. N. (1967). *Anat. Rec.* **159**, 231–238.
Low, F. N. (1968). *Anat. Rec.* **160**, 93–108.
Low, F. N. (1970). *Amer. J. Anat.* **128**, 45–56.
Lowther, D. A., Toole, B. P., and Herrington, A. C. (1970). In "Chemistry and Molecular Biology of the Intercellular Matrix" (E. A. Balazs, ed.), Vol. 2, pp. 1135–1153. Academic Press, New York.
Luft, J. H. (1971). *Anat. Rec.* **171**, 369.
Manasek, F. J. (1968). *J. Morphol.* **125**, 329–366.
Manasek, F. J. (1970). *J. Exp. Zool.* **174**, 415–440.
Manasek, F. J. (1973). In "Developmental Regulation. Aspects of Cell Differentiation" (S. Coward, ed.), pp. 193–218. Academic Press, New York.

Manasek, F. J. (1975). *In* "Developmental Aspects of Cardiac Cellular Physiology" (M. Lieberman and T. Sano, eds.). Raven Press, New York. (In press.)

Manasek, F. J., Reid, M., Vinson, W., Seyer, J., and Johnson, R. (1973). *Develop. Biol.* **35**, 332–348.

Markwald, R. R., and Adams Smith, W. N. (1972). *J. Histochem. Cytochem.* **20**, 896–907.

Martin, G. R., Piez, K. A., and Lewis, M. S. (1963). *Biochim. Biophys. Acta* **69**, 472–479.

Martínez-Palomo, A. (1970). *Int. Rev. Cytol.* **29**, 29–75.

Marzuilo, G., and Lash, J. W. (1970). *Develop. Biol.* **22**, 638–654.

Mathews, M. B. (1970). *In* "Chemistry and Molecular Biology of the Intercellular Matrix" (E. A. Balazs, ed.), Vol. 2, pp. 1155–1169. Academic Press, New York.

Mathews, M. B., and Glagov, S. (1966). *J. Clin. Invest.* **45**, 1103–1111.

Meier, S., and Hay, E. D. (1973). *Develop. Biol.* **35**, 318–331.

Meyer, K., Hoffman, P., and Linker, A. (1960). *In* "The Enzymes" (P. D. Boyer, H. Lardy, and K. Myrbäck, eds.), 2nd ed., Vol. 4, Part A, pp. 447–460. Academic Press, New York.

Miller, E. J. (1971a). *Biochemistry* **10**, 1652–1659.

Miller, E. J. (1971b). *Biochemistry* **10**, 3030–3034.

Miller, E. J. (1971c). *Fed. Proc., Fed. Amer. Soc. Exp. Biol.* **28**, 1839–1945.

Miller, E. J., and Matukas, V. (1969). *Proc. Nat. Acad. Sci. U.S.* **64**, 1264–1268.

Miller, E. J., Martin, G. R., Piez, K. A., and Powers, M. J. (1967). *J. Biol. Chem.* **242**, 5481–5489.

Miller, E. J., Lane, J. M., and Piez, K. A. (1969). *Biochemistry* **8**, 30–39.

Miller, E. J., Epstein, E. H., and Piez, K. A. (1971). *Biochem. Biophys. Res. Commun.* **42**, 1024–1029.

Miller, E. J., Woodall, D. L., and Vail, M. S. (1973). *J. Biol. Chem.* **248**, 1666–1671.

Nagai, Y., Gross, J., and Piez, K. A. (1964). *Ann. N.Y. Acad. Sci.* **121**, 494–500.

Nameroff, M., and Holtzer, H. (1967). *Develop. Biol.* **16**, 250–281.

Narayanan, A. S., Siegel, R. C., and Martin, G. R. (1972). *Biochem. Biophys. Res. Commun.* **46**, 745–751.

New, D. A. T. (1955). *J. Embryol. Exp. Morphol.* **3**, 320–331.

Nimni, M. E. (1965). *Biochim. Biophys. Acta* **111**, 576–579.

Nold, J. G., Kang, A. H., and Gross, J. (1970). *Science* **170**, 1096–1098.

Öbrink, B. (1970). *In* "Chemistry and Molecular Biology of the Intercellular Matrix" (E. A. Balazs, ed.), Vol. 2, pp. 1171–1178. Academic Press, New York.

O'Hare, M. J. (1973). *J. Embryol. Exp. Morphol.* **29**, 197–208.

Pal, S., Doganges, P. T., and Schubert, M. (1966). *J. Biol. Chem.* **241**, 4261–4266.

Palmoski, M. J., and Goetinck, P. T. (1972). *Proc. Nat. Acad. Sci. U.S.* **69**, 3385–3388.

Pease, D. C. (1966). *J. Ultrastruct. Res.* **15**, 555–588.

Peterkofsky, B. (1972). *Arch. Biochem. Biophys.* **152**, 318–328.

Pierce, G. B. (1970). *In* "Chemistry and Molecular Biology of the Intercellular Matrix" (E. A. Balazs, ed.), Vol. 1, pp. 471–506. Academic Press, New York.

Piez, K. A., Weiss, E., and Lewis, M. S. (1960). *J. Biol. Chem.* **235**, 1987–1991.

Piez, K. A., Eigner, E. A., and Lewis, M. S. (1963). *Biochemistry* **2**, 58–66.

Piez, K. A., Martin, G. R., Kang, A. H., and Bornstein, P. (1966). *Biochemistry* **5**, 3813–3820.

Piez, K. A., Miller, E. J., Lane, J. M., and Butler, W. T. (1969). *Biochem. Biophys. Res. Commun.* **37**, 801–805.

Quintarelli, G., Scott, J. E., and Dellovo, M. C. (1964). *Histochemie* **4**, 99–112.

Rambourg, A. (1969). *J. Microsc.* (*Paris*) **8**, 325–341.
Rambourg, A. (1971). *Int. Rev. Cytol.* **31**, 57–114.
Rambourg, A., and Leblond, C. P. (1967). *J. Cell Biol.* **32**, 27–53.
Rambourg, A., Neutra, M., and Leblond, C. P. (1966). *Anat. Rec.* **154**, 41–71.
Revel, J.-P., and Goodenough, D. A. (1970). *In* "Chemistry and Molecular Biology of the Intercellular Matrix" (E. A. Balazs, ed.), Vol. 3, pp. 1361–1380. Academic Press, New York.
Robinson, H. C., and Dorfman, A. (1969). *J. Biol. Chem.* **244**, 348–352.
Rodén, L. (1970). *In* "Chemistry and Molecular Biology of the Intercellular Matrix" (E. A. Balazs, ed.), Vol. 2, pp. 797–821. Academic Press, New York.
Roseman, S. (1970). *Chem. Phys. Lipids* **5**, 270–297.
Rosenberg, L. (1973). *Fed. Proc., Fed. Amer. Soc. Exp. Biol.* **32**, 1467–1473.
Rosenberg, L., and Schubert, M. (1967). *J. Biol. Chem.* **242**, 4697–4701.
Rosenberg, L., Pal, S., and Beale, R., and Schubert, M. (1970). *J. Biol. Chem.* **245**, 4112–4122.
Sadjera, S., and Hascall, V. (1969). *J. Biol. Chem.* **244**, 77–87.
Saito, H., Yamagata, T., and Suzuki, S. (1968). *J. Biol. Chem.* **243**, 1536–1542.
Schubert, M., and Hamerman, D. (1956). *J. Histochem. Cytochem.* **4**, 159–189.
Schubert, M., and Hamerman, D. (1968). "A Primer on Connective Tissue Biochemistry." Lea & Febiger, Philadelphia, Pennsylvania.
Schulman, H. J., and Meyer, K. (1968). *J. Exp. Med.* **128**, 1353–1362.
Schulman, H. J., and Meyer, K. (1970). *Biochem. J.* **120**, 689–697.
Scott, J. E., and Dorling, J. (1965). *Histochemie* **5**, 221–233.
Searls, R. L. (1973a). *In* "Developmental Regulation: Aspects of Cell Differentiation" (S. J. Coward, ed.), pp. 219–251. Academic Press, New York.
Searls (1973b). *Clin. Orthop. Relat. Res.* **96**, 327–344.
Sharon, N. (1966). *Annu. Rev. Biochem.* **35**, 485.
Shur, B., and Roth, S. (1973). *Amer. Zool.* **13**, 1129–1135.
Silbert, J. E., and Deluca, S. (1969). *J. Biol. Chem.* **244**, 876–881.
Spicer, S. S. (1960). *J. Histochem. Cytochem.* **8**, 18–36.
Spicer, S. S. (1963). *Ann. N.Y. Acad. Sci.* **106**, 379–388.
Spicer, S. S., Horn, R. G., and Leppi, T. J. (1967). *In* "The Connective Tissues" (B. M. Wagner and D. E. Smith, eds.), pp. 251–303. Williams & Wilkins, Baltimore, Maryland.
Spiro, R. G. (1970a). *In* "Chemistry and Molecular Biology of the Intercellular Matrix" (E. A. Balazs, ed.), Vol. I, pp. 195–215. Adademic Press, New York.
Spiro, R. G. (1970b). *Annu. Rev. Biochem.* **39**, 599–638.
Stegemann, H. (1958). *Hoppe-Seyler's Z. Physiol. Chem.* **311**, 41–45.
Tanford, C., Marler, E., Jury, E., and Davidson, E. A. (1964). *J. Biol. Chem.* **239**, 4034–4040.
Tanzer, M. L. (1965). *Int. Rev. Connect. Tissue Res.* **3**, 9–112.
Tanzer, M. L. (1973). *Science* **180**, 561–566.
Telser, A., Robinson, H. C., and Dorfman, A. (1965). *Proc. Nat. Acad. Sci. U.S.* **54**, 912–919.
Thorp, F. K., and Dorfman, A. (1963). *J. Cell Biol.* **18**, 13–17.
Thyberg, J., Lohmander, S., and Friberg, U. (1973). *J. Ultrastruct. Res.* **45**, 407–427.
Toole, B. P. (1969). *Nature* (*London*) **222**, 872–873.
Toole, B. P. (1972). *Develop. Biol.* **29**, 321–329.
Toole, B. P. (1973). *Amer. Zool.* **13**, 1061–1065.
Toole, B. P., and Lowther, D. A. (1968). *Biochem. J.* **109**, 857–866.

Toole, B. P., and Trelstad, R. L. (1971). *Develop. Biol.* **26**, 28–35.

Toole, B. P., Kang, A. H., Trelstad, R. L., and Gross, J. (1972). *Biochem. J.* **127**, 715–720.

Traub, W., and Piez, K. A. (1971). *Advan. Protein Chem.* **25**, 243–352.

Trelstad, R. L., Kang, A. H., Igarshi, F., and Gross, J. (1970). *Biochemistry* **9**, 4993–4998.

Trelstad, R. L., Kang, A. H., Toole, B. P., and Gross, J. (1972). *J. Biol. Chem.* **247**, 6469–6473.

Trelstad, R. L., Kang, A. H., Cohen, A. M., and Hay, E. D. (1973). *Science* **179**, 295–297.

Trelstad, R. L., Hayashi, K., and Toole, B. P. (1974). *J. Cell Biol.* **62**, 815–830.

Volpin, D., and Veis, A. (1971). *Biochem. Biophys. Res. Commun.* **44**, 804–812.

Volpin, D., and Veis, A. (1973). *Biochemistry* **12**, 1452–1464.

von Hippel, P. H., and Harrington, W. F. (1960). *Brookhaven Symp. Biol.* **13**, 213–231.

Vuust, J., Lane, J. M., Fietzek, P. P., Miller, E. J., and Piez, K. A. (1970). *Biochem. Biophys. Res. Commun.* **38**, 703–710.

Weber, K., and Osborn, M. (1969). *J. Biol. Chem.* **244**, 4406–4412.

Wessler, E. (1970). *In* "Chemistry and Molecular Biology of the Intercellular Matrix" (E. A. Balazs, ed.), Vol. 2, pp. 895–901. Academic Press, New York.

White, A., Handler, P., and Smith, G. L. (1964). "Principles of Biochemistry," p. 633. McGraw-Hill, New York.

Yamagata, T., Saito, H., Habuchi, O., and Suzuki, S. (1968). *J. Biol. Chem.* **248**, 1523–1535.

Zwaan, J., and Hendrix, R. (1973). *Amer. Zool.* **13**, 1039–1049.

CHAPTER 3

THE ROLE OF THE GOLGI COMPLEX DURING SPERMIOGENESIS

Baccio Baccetti

INSTITUTE OF ZOOLOGY, UNIVERSITY OF SIENA, SIENA, ITALY

I. Introduction

The studies on the synthesis of macromolecules during spermatogenesis in *Drosophila* have shown that RNA synthesis is completed in the spermatocyte (Olivieri and Olivieri, 1965; Henning, 1967) and that after meiosis the nucleus is practically inactive. A weak postmeiotic RNA synthesis has been detected in Orthoptera (Bloch and Brack, 1964; Henderson, 1964; Muckenthaler, 1964) and in rats (Monesi, 1965); this is, however, of brief duration. Therefore the only RNA detectable in the spermatid is in the cytoplasm, and the whole protein synthesis that occurs at this stage is directed by templates transcribed before completion of meiosis.

The common pattern in insects is generally of the *Drosophila* type: X sperms and Y sperms are similar, the absence or rupture of Y produces the same deformations in the populations of both sperms (Bairati and Baccetti, 1966; Hess and Meyer, 1968; Kiefer, 1969); the loss of the nucleus during the spermatid stage in Lepidoptera apyrene sperms does not cause the loss of any of the tail organelles (Phillips, 1971). Hence, the precursors of the organelles whose morphogenesis starts in the more advanced stages of spermiogenesis must have been present in the cytoplasm of the spermatid since before the loss of the nucleus. Typical is the case of the acrosome that arises from a conspicuous Golgi complex (Fig. 1), which is already detectable in the young spermatid.

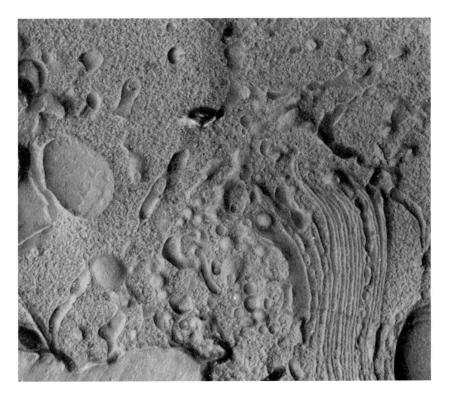

Fig. 1. The Golgi complex in insect spermatid (*Tenebrio molitor*). Freeze-etching, Philips 301. ×37,500 (original).

Other accessory organelles are present in the more evoluted sperm patterns, such as those of the insects and of the vertebrates. The investigations made in our laboratory have dealt primarily with the insects, where the variety of accessory structures is the highest. We have demonstrated that even the crystalline rods of mitochondrial derivatives, the extra-axoneme accessory bodies, the content of the 9 accessory tubules (see Section III, B) of the axoneme, and in many cases even the limiting membrane of the mature sperm, besides other accessory organelles typical of certain spermatozoa, are entirely or at least partially formed by the Golgi complex; in any case, they reach completion through the active participation of the Golgi complex. The data are summarized in this review.

II. Secretion of the Acrosome

The acrosome is the most typical organelle produced by the Golgi complex. Its activity was clearly demonstrated by Bowen in 1924 with the light microscope. The first important electron microscopic observations were made on mammals by Burgos and Fawcett (1955) and by Fawcett and Hollenberg (1963); they were able to follow the progressive formation of the acrosome, of the acrosomal vesicle and granule and of the proacrosomal granules from the Golgi complex. The secretory activity starts in the concave side of the organelle; only in one insect has the formation of the acrosomal granule been found to occur in its convex side (Phillips, 1970).

Many types of spermatozoa have cone-shaped acrosomes with a rodlet inside them (that in amphibians and birds is named perforatorium) and a layer of periacrosomal material at the outside. The origin of such structures is still obscure and the participation of the Golgi complex in this formation is not clearly demonstrated. On the other hand, there is a general consensus that in all animals the Golgi complex is the only structure directly responsible for the formation of the acrosome. It is important to stress that the formation of the acrosome precursor, the proacrosomal granule, is due to the activity of the vesicles and vacuoles located in the Golgi area. In the insects studied by Kaye (1962) and by us (Baccetti et al., 1969b, 1970), for example, many minute vesicles arising from the Golgi merge in a homogeneous, spheroid proacrosomal granule bounded by a typical membrane. The granule grows within the Golgi region (the so-called acroblast) and progressively acquires the shape of the acrosome.

III. Formation of the Inner Spermatid Membranes and Their Derivatives

During the processes leading to the formation of the acrosome and to the shaping up of the nucleus and of the mitochondria, a rich system of flattened cisternae with smooth membranes differentiates around the spermatid organelles (Figs. 2 and 3). Those who first detected them in mammals and insects interpreted them as endoplasmic reticulum (Burgos and Ishida, 1958; Ito, 1960; Shay and Biesele, 1968). This interpretation, however, is not generally accepted and other investigators prefer the noncommittal description of smooth cytoplasmic membranes (Baccetti and Bairati, 1964; Bawa, 1964; Warner, 1971) or "tail membranes" (Rothschild, 1955) or axonemal sheaths (Stanley et al., 1972); Tokuyasu,

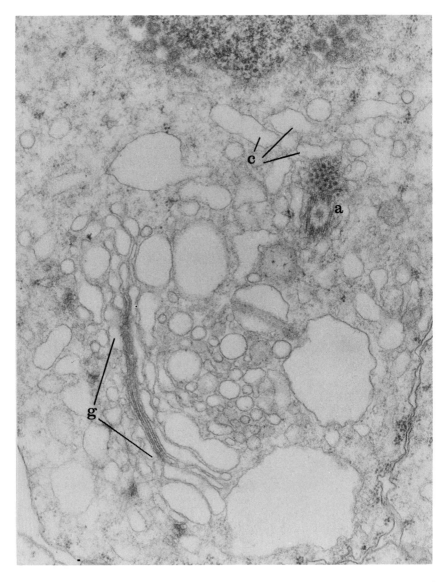

FIG. 2. *Bacillus rossius* spermatid: several cisternae (c) derived from the Golgi complex (g) surround the axoneme (a). Philips 301. ×30,000. From Baccetti *et al.* (1973a).

1974). The derivation of these membranes from the Golgi complex (Sakai and Shigenaga, 1967) rather than from evaginations of the nuclear envelope seems to be ascertained.

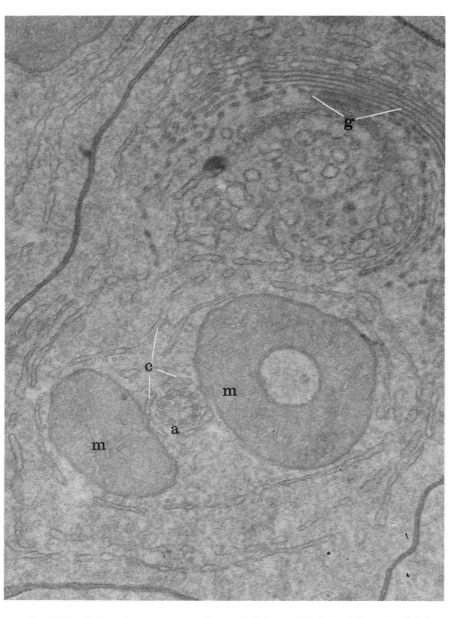

FIG. 3. *Tenebrio molitor* spermatid: flattened cisternae (c) derived from the Golgi complex (g) surround axoneme (a) and mitochondrial derivatives (m). Thiéry PAS–PTA staining for polysaccharides; Philips 301. ×50,000. By courtesy of R. Dallai.

Only few authors suggest the Golgi origin of the endoplasmic reticulum (Manton, 1960; Sakai and Shigenaga, 1967); in general, it is considered as the extension of the nuclear envelope (Watson, 1955; Epstein, 1957; Porter and Machado, 1960; and others). The rough fraction and the smooth fraction exhibited in this system are intercommunicating (Porter, 1961); in fact, the smooth fraction seems to arise from the rough reticulum (Jones and Fawcett, 1966). The continuity of the cytomembrane system seems to proceed from the endoplasmic reticulum toward the Golgi complex (Porter, 1961; Whaley *et al.*, 1964; Goldblatt, 1969; and others) suggesting that the latter derives from the former. Considering all this, the term endoplasmic reticulum does not seem appropriate for describing the system of smooth membranes present in the insect spermatid; a more correct definition is Golgi-derived membranes (Baccetti, 1972; Baccetti *et al.*, 1973b). These membranes surround the organelles which differentiate in the spermatid and sometimes even the whole complex of the definitive structures of the spermatozoon. Their progressive relationship to the single systems suggests a morphogenetic role.

A. GOLGI-DERIVED CISTERNAE AND MITOCHONDRIAL DERIVATIVES

The rearrangement of the spermatid chondriome in two elongated structures flanking the axoneme is typical of pterygote insects. Once the two mitochondrial derivatives have reached their full dimensions and definitive position, longitudinally oriented protein filaments start gathering inside them (Baccetti *et al.*, 1973b); in the mature sperm this material takes up a crystalline organization with a general period of 450 Å. Sometimes it fills up both derivatives or may occupy only a portion of them (general reviews, in Phillips, 1970; Baccetti, 1972). In a work on *Tenebrio* (Baccetti *et al.*, 1973b) we illustrated the formation of the crystalline material [also in some figures of Warner (1971) on *Sarcophaga*]. The crystalline material begins to appear at the time the two flattened Golgi-derived cisternae come into contact with the mitochondrial wall, and occupies the very spot where the contact occurs (Fig. 4). The cisterna flattens and joins the outer membrane of the mitochondrial derivative, where the space between the two membranes is narrower. At this point electron-opaque material unstainable with histochemical methods is also present inside the cisterna and in the space between the two membranes, and the first osmophilic filaments appear inside the mitochondrial matrix. Although the nature of the material transferred from the cisternae to the mitochondrion is, as yet, unknown, a correlation between the Golgi complex and the mitochondrial changes seems to be certain.

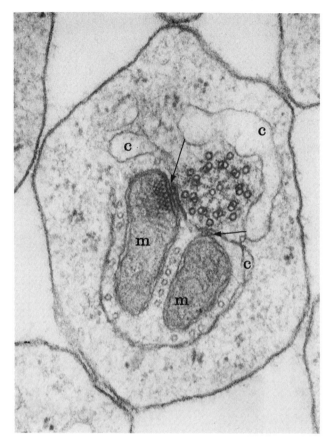

FIG. 4. *Tenebrio* spermatid. Flat Golgi-derived cisternae (c) make contact with the mitochondrial wall (arrows). Crystalline material starts gathering into the mitochondrial derivatives (m). Philips 301. ×75,000. By courtesy of F. Giusti.

B. GOLGI-DERIVED CISTERNAE AND ACCESSORY TUBULES

Inside the maturing spermatid of insects, outside of the 9 doublets of the axoneme, 9 accessory tubules are formed. This kind of symmetric accessory structures (the so-called outer, or coarse, fibers) is characteristic of almost all spermatozoa of the animals with internal fertilization. In many insects, the tubules become gradually filled up with glycoprotein material that either persists until maturity or disappears at some time during the process of maturation (Baccetti, 1972). In *Bacillus rossius* (Baccetti *et al.*, 1973a), while this material is laid down, the Golgi complex encircles the axoneme with its tiny cisternae and adheres to accessory tubules 7, 8, and 9, thus maintaining a 9 symmetry; on the other hand, the Golgi vesicles corresponding to fibers 2, 3, and 4 are fused together in one single flat cisterna (Fig. 5). Direct contacts between tubules and cisternae are evident, and the participation of the Golgi com-

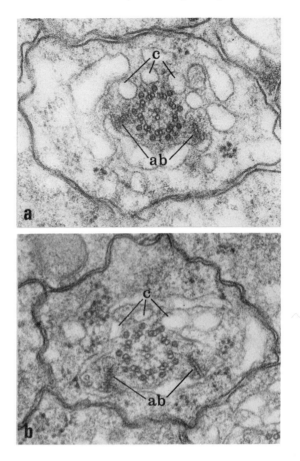

FIG. 5. Two consecutive stages (a, b) of *Bacillus rossius* spermatid maturation. The Golgi-derived cisternae (c) encircle the axoneme maintaining a 9 symmetry adhering to the accessory tubules 7, 8, and 9. From the flat cisterna corresponding to tubules 2, 3, and 4, the accessory bodies (ab) arise. Philips 301. ×60,000. From Baccetti *et al.* (1973a).

plex in the supply of glycoproteins to the tubules seems probable. Also in *Tenebrio* cisternae with the same arrangement can be seen, and contacts are evident (Fig. 6). The same happens in several Diptera whose spermatids have been studied (Baccetti and Bairati, 1964; Warner, 1971; Stanley *et al.*, 1972; and others).

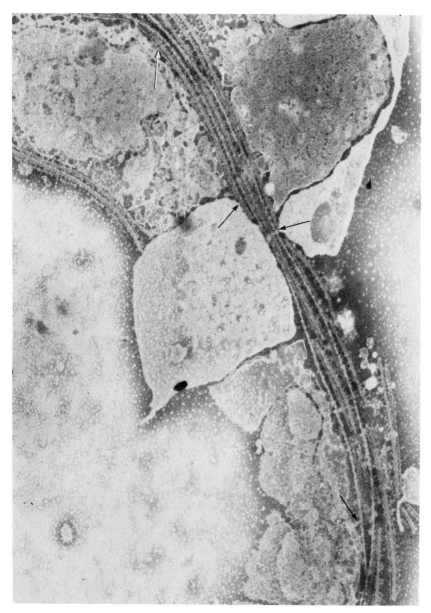

FIG. 6. *Tenebrio molitor*. The conspicuous Golgi complex surrounding the axoneme, after negative staining. Contacts between cisternae and accessory tubules are indicated by arrows. Philips 301. ×48,000. By courtesy of F. Rosati.

C. GOLGI-DERIVED CISTERNAE AND ORDINATE EXTRA-AXONEMAL ACCESSORY BODIES

Two glycoprotein accessory bodies with a well defined crisscross crystalline pattern have been described; they flank the axoneme like the mitochondrial derivatives in the spermatozoa of many orders of Pterygota insects (for a review, see Baccetti, 1972). These bodies give a positive ATPase and UTPase reaction and appear to play a role in the flagellar motility of the insect spermatozoa; they are most apparent in Phasmoidea in which no mitochondria are present (Baccetti *et al.*, 1973a) and in Ephemeroptera, whose mitochondrial derivatives are devoid of crystalline ordered protein filaments (Baccetti *et al.*, 1969a). In both cases, as well as in Coleoptera (Baccetti *et al.*, 1973b) and Hemiptera (Mazzini, 1970) where mitochondrial derivatives filled with crystalline ordered protein filaments coexist with extra-axonemal bodies, a precise role of the Golgi-derived cisternae has been demonstrated during their formation inside the spermatid. In particular, in *Bacillus rossius* the progressive development of the laminae which give rise to the accessory bodies starting from the two bilaminar protrusions in two Golgi-derived cisternae (Figs. 5 and 7) has been clearly described (Baccetti *et al.*, 1973a). The two cisternae move still farther apart from one another and each of them sends out, on either side of the previous protruding bilaminar process, two parallel laminar processes. This results in the formation of a stratified complex of four laminae, each of them made up of longitudinal and transversal fibers.

Other typical extra-axoneme accessory components are the double periaxoneme ring and the axial rod that keeps the undulated membrane flat inside the spermatozoon of urodele amphibians. The origin and the role of these structures are not well understood (Fawcett, 1970). It has been suggested (Werner, 1969, 1970) that in the spermatid a dictyosome that originates from the Golgi complex that gives rise to the acrosome moves toward the centriolar region, where it deposits a material round the ring and the axial rod. Thus, according to this author, the Golgi complex should participate in the formation of several sperm organelles. In the light of the observations in insects, this seems very likely; however, when the axial rod is similar to the accessory body No. 3 of mammal spermatozoa, a direct origin from the Golgi appears to be rather improbable (Fawcett, 1970; Picheral, 1972).

D. GOLGI-DERIVED CISTERNAE AND PLASMA MEMBRANE

As a rule, during the rearrangement of the cellular structures throughout spermiogenesis a conspicuous loss of cytoplasmic material occurs. The area of the membrane of the spermatozoon is therefore smaller than that of the original spermatid of which, nevertheless, it is a part. This has

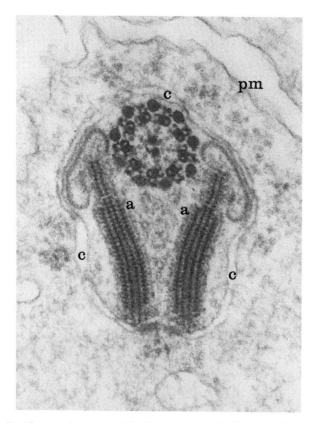

FIG. 7. *Bacillus rossius* spermatid. The accessory bodies (a) derived from the flat Golgi cisternae are almost completed, but still in contact with it. All the cisternae are fused together around the tail organelles (c). The old spermatid plasma membrane (pm) coexists. Philips 301. ×80,000. From Baccetti *et al.* (1973a).

been shown in some cases in the Orthoptera, where the formation of a brush-shaped glycocalyx arises while the spermatid is in the roundish stage (Baccetti *et al.*, 1971). In other cases the membrane is suddenly and almost entirely lost during the last stages of spermiogenesis. In *Bacillus* (Baccetti *et al.*, 1973a) large flattened cisternae originating from the Golgi complex surround either the axoneme (Figs. 7 and 8) and its accessory bodies, or the anterior region of the nucleus. Eventually these cisternae split (Fig. 9) and shed cytoplasmic vesicles whose outer wall is made up by the original plasma membrane while the inside lining is made up by the outer wall of the Golgi cisternae. The definitive plasma membrane thus gives rise to the inner wall of the cisternae, while what was once the inner surface of the Golgi cisternae becomes the outer surface of the spermatozoon (Fig. 10). In *Tenebrio* this process is even more apparent: here the rudimentary spermatozoon inside the spermatid is

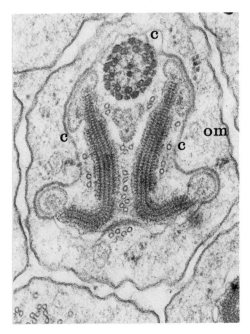

FIG. 8. *Bacillus rossius* spermatid. The flattened Golgi-derived cisterna (c) is completed around the tail inside the old membrane (om). Philips 301. ×60,000. From Baccetti *et al.* (1973a).

entirely encircled by the Golgi cisternae (Fig. 11), and the spermatozoon surrounded by the new membrane emerges from the old cytoplasm as from a cylinder (Fig. 12). The new and the old membrane coexist for a long time with similar characteristics (Fig. 13) and surround the whole spermatozoon, separated from one another by a cytoplasmic layer that will soon disappear.

IV. Direct Formation of Peripheral Organelles in Aberrant Spermatozoa

It is known that in some of the more evolved orders many phyla undergo a peculiar regression of the motility organs of the spermatozoon which becomes aflagellate and sometimes differentiates substitutive organelles. In some cases certain peripheral organelles persist throughout the life of the spermatozoon, but as a rule they are seen to degenerate as soon as they enter the female genital tracts.

A. THE "SPONGY CHAMBERS"

In the spermatozoa of Diplopoda these grooved spongy organelles are located just beneath the surface of some areas; they communicate with

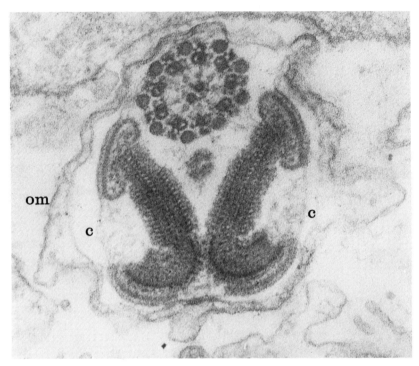

Fig. 9. *Bacillus rossius* mature spermatid. The Golgi-derived cisterna (c) splits. Its outer wall delimitates the residual cytoplasm which is externally limited by the old plasma membrane (om). Philips 301. ×100,000. From Baccetti *et al.* (1973a).

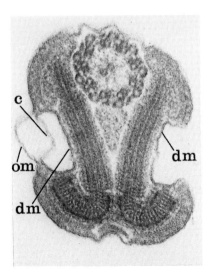

Fig. 10. *Bacillus rossius* spermatozoon. Elimination of the old membrane (om) together with the outer wall of the Golgi-derived cisterna (c). The definitive Golgi-derived membrane (dm) is just deposited. Philips 301. ×100,000. From Baccetti *et al.* (1973a).

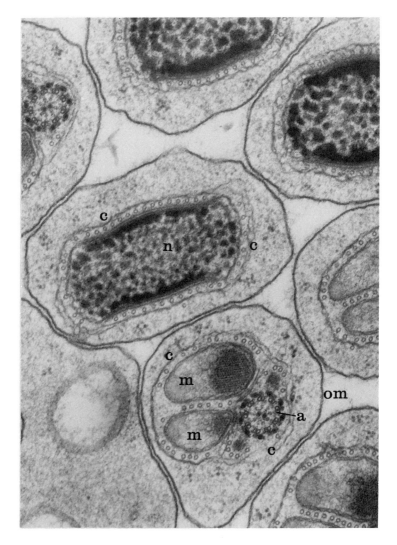

FIG. 11. *Tenebrio molitor* spermatid. Nuclei (n) and tail organelles (a, axoneme; m, mitochondria; ab, accessory bodies) are completely encircled by the Golgi-derived cisternae (c) and the old spermatid plasma membrane (om). Philips 301. ×45,000. By courtesy of F. Rosati.

the outside through one single opening (Baccetti *et al.*, 1974). They are typical of barrel-shaped sperms. As soon as the spermatozoa become rib-bonlike inside the female tracts, the spongy chambers are expelled and give rise to a membranous mass around the spermatozoon. It is suggested that they ensure free exchange between the spermatozoa and their neigh-

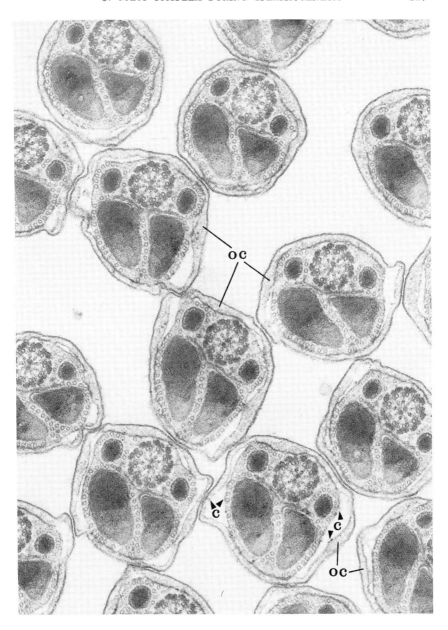

FIG. 12. *Tenebrio molitor* mature spermatids. The sperm organelles are entirely encircled by the Golgi-derived cisterna (c), that starts splitting (arrows) and the sperm emerges from the old cytoplasm (oc). Philips 301. ×45,000. By courtesy of R. Dallai.

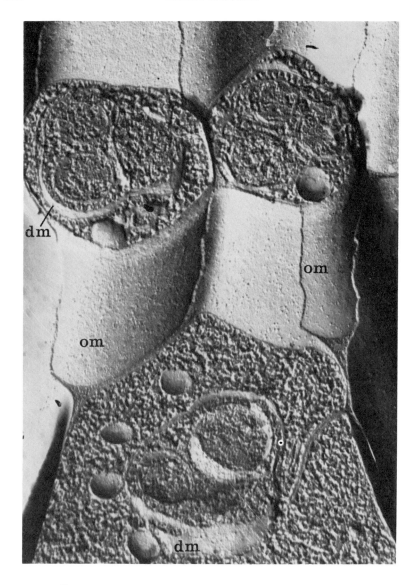

Fɪɢ. 13. *Tenebrio molitor*. Same stage. Definitive (dm) and old (om) membranes show a similar structure. Freeze-etching, Philips 301. ×60,000. (original).

boring organelles. Like other tiny organelles (the so-called X body, the proteic laminae reinforcing the inner aspect of the plasma membrane, the vestibules of the "spongy chambers") in the same cell, they originate from the Golgi complex during the spermatid stage (Fig. 14). Although not directly involved in motility (in fact, the sperm is very likely im-

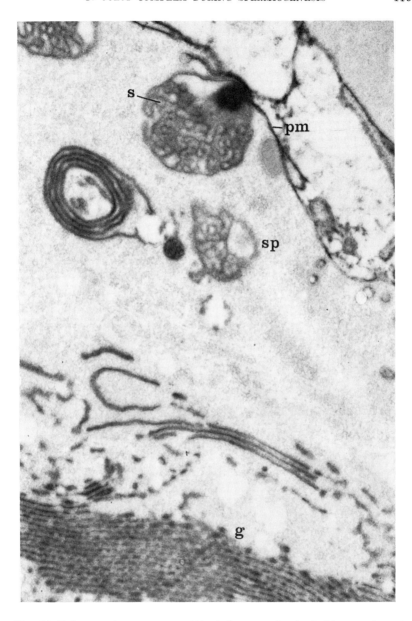

FIG. 14. *Polyxenus largurus* spermatid. A "spongy chamber" (s) open into the plasma membrane (pm) and a precursor of it (sp) arising from the Golgi complex (g). Thiéry PAS–PTA staining for polysaccharides. Philips 301. ×30,000. From Baccetti *et al.* (1974).

motile), the spongy chambers form a peripheral organ which is typical of many kinds of immotile sperms; for example, in Nematoda (Jamuar, 1966; Foor, 1968; Beams and Sekhon, 1972; Pasternak and Samoiloff, 1972) and, with but slight differences, in the aflagellate spermatozoa of the fish *Gymnarchus niloticus* (Mattei *et al.*, 1967). Its origin is still not precisely known; it is described as a mitochondrion-like organ (Jamuar, 1966) or as a specialization of the cellular membrane (Foor, 1968); or as a derivative of the Golgi complex (Beams and Sekhon, 1972). The case is therefore similar to that of Diplopoda.

B. MICROVILLI ON THE MEMBRANE OF TICK SPERMATOZOA

Reger (1962) was the first to discover the layer of microvillous outgrowths on the plasma membrane in the posterior part of aflagellate tick spermatozoa. His discovery was soon confirmed by many authors, and most convincingly by Breucker and Horstmann (1972). The latter authors asserted also that such protrusions are due to the pressure exerted by small cytoplasmic cisternae against the plasma membrane. The origin of such cytoplasmic cisternae is uncertain, although Reger's figures (1962) clearly suggest that they arise from the Golgi complex. Similar protrusions have been described by Graebner and Adam (1970) in gnatostomulid turbellarian sperms. They also originate from the Golgi complex.

V. Conclusions

The observations presented in this paper point to the importance of the role played by the Golgi complex in the formation of almost all the structures present in the more evolved spermatozoa. The only exceptions are the centriolar derivatives (centriole adjunct, axoneme, accessory fibers) and the mitochondria. It is true that the latter (as in the pterygote insects) collect abundant paracrystalline protein materials through direct contacts with the Golgi complex.

The evidence thus is that all the structures of the spermatozoon are already in the young spermatid whose nucleus is inactive, and that they are formed at the same time. The better known process of Golgian secretion, that of the acrosome, is therefore applicable to many other organelles which are typical of more complex models of spermatozoa. The acrosome, considered as the only Golgi product, characterizes the primitive spermatozoa, as, for instance, those of the echinoderms. The most important fact, and of general value, is the complete participation of the Golgi complex in the total simultaneous substitution of the membrane, as seen in Coleoptera spermatozoa. The key role played by the Golgi complex in the production of the plasma membrane is generally accepted (Sjöstrand, 1968; Morré *et al.*, 1971) even though most components are assembled *in loco*, in particular during the interphase (Graham *et al.*, 1973). Besides the Golgi complex influences the organization of the cell surface through the synthesis of carbohydrates for the glycocalyx (Whaley *et al.*, 1972). The process described here whereby the new definitive membrane originates by the splitting of a cylindrical Golgi cisterna and by the exposure of an external glycocalyx (made up of the glycoproteins that were inside the same cisterna) seems the best and most convincing demonstration of this. Another, though less dramatic, process is the expansion of the old membrane as a result of its fusion with Golgi cisternae; this process is typical of the tick spermatozoa (Reger, 1962).

VI. Summary

In this paper the importance of the Golgi complex in the formation of almost all the structures typical of the more evolved sperm types is stressed. In the primitive types of sperm, the Golgi is clearly associated only with the secretion of the acrosome, whereas axoneme, nucleus, and mitochondria have obviously a different and independent origin. But the accessory organelles characteristic of the more evolved sperm types (crystalline rod of mitochondrial derivatives, glycoprotein content of accessory tubules, ordinate accessory bodies, definitive plasma membrane with related organelles) are formed in close association with Golgi activity.

REFERENCES

Baccetti, B. (1972). *Advan. Insect Physiol.*, **9**, 315.
Baccetti, B., and Bairati, A., Jr. (1964). *"Redia"* **49**, 1.
Baccetti, B., Dallai, R., and Giusti, F. (1969a). *J. Ultrastruct. Res.* **29**, 343.
Baccetti, B., Dallai, R., and Rosati, F. (1969b). *J. Microsc. (Paris)* **8**, 233.
Baccetti, B., Dallai, R., and Rosati, F. (1970). *J. Ultrastruct. Res.* **31**, 312.
Baccetti, B., Bigliardi, E., and Rosati, F. (1971). *J. Ultrastruct. Res.* **35**, 582.
Baccetti, B., Burrini, A. G., Dallai, R., Pallini, V., Periti, P., Piantelli, F., Rosati, F., and Selmi, G. (1973a). *J. Ultrastruct. Res., Suppl.* **12**, 1.
Baccetti, B., Burrini, A. G., Dallai, R., Giusti, F., Mazzini, M., Renieri, T., Rosati, F., and Selmi, G. (1973b). *J. Mechanochem. Cell Motility* **2**, 149.
Baccetti, B., Dallai, R., Bernini, F., and Mazzini, M. (1974). *J. Morphol.* **143**, 187.
Bairati, A., Jr., and Baccetti, B. (1966). *Drosophila Inform. Serv.* **41**, 152.
Bawa, S. R. (1964). *J. Cell Biol.* **23**, 431.
Beams, H. W., and Sekhon, S. S. (1972). *J. Ultrastruct. Res.* **38**, 511.
Bloch, D. P., and Brack, S. D. (1964). *J. Cell Biol.* **22**, 337.
Bowen, R. H. (1924). *J. Morphol.* **39**, 351.
Breucker, H., and Horstmann, E. (1972). *Z. Zellforsch. Mikrosk. Anat.* **123**, 18.
Burgos, M. H., and Fawcett, D. W. (1955). *J. Biophys. Biochem. Cytol.* **1**, 287.
Epstein, M. A. (1957). *J. Biophys. Biochem. Cytol.* **3**, 851.
Favard, P. (1969). *In* "Handbook of Molecular Cytology" (A. Lima-de-Faria, ed.), p. 1130. North-Holland Publ., Amsterdam.
Fawcett, D. W. (1970). *Biol. Reprod.* **2**, 90.

Fawcett, D. W., and Hollenberg, R. D. (1963). *Z. Zellforsch. Mikrosk. Anat.* **60**, 276.
Foor, W. E. (1968). *J. Cell Biol.* **39**, 119.
Goldblatt, P. J. (1969). In "Handbook of Molecular Cytology" (A. Lima-de-Faria, ed.), p. 1101. North-Holland Publ., Amsterdam.
Graham, J. M., Summer, M. C. B., Curtis, D. H., and Pasternak, C. A. (1973). *Nature (London)* **246**, 291.
Graebner, J., and Adam, H. (1970). In "Comparative Spermatology" (B. Baccetti, ed.), p. 375.
Henderson, S. A. (1964). *Chromosoma* **15**, 345.
Henning, W. (1967). *Chromosoma* **22**, 294.
Hess, O., and Meyer, G. F. (1968). *J. Cell Biol.* **16**, 527.
Ito, S. (1960). *J. Biophys. Biochem. Cytol.* **7**, 433.
Jamuar, M. P. (1966). *J. Cell Biol.* **31**, 381.
Jones, A. L., and Fawcett, D. W. (1966). *J. Histochem. Cytochem.* **14**, 215.
Kaye, J. S. (1962). *J. Cell Biol.* **12**, 411.
Kiefer, B. I. (1969). *Genetics* **61**, 157.
Manton, I. (1960). *J. Biophys. Biochem. Cytol.* **8**, 221.
Mattei, X., Boisson, C., Mattei, C., and Reizer, C. (1967). *C. Acad. Sci.* **265**, 2010.
Mazzini, M. (1970). *Atti Accad. Fisiocr. Siena* [14] **2**, 1.
Monesi, V. (1965). *Exp. Cell Res.* **39**, 197.
Morré, D. J., Mollenhauer, H. H., and Bracker, C. (1971). In "Origin and Continuity of Cell Organelles" (W. Beermann, J. Reinert, and Ursprung, eds.), p. 82.
Muckenthaler, F. A. (1964). *Exp. Cell Res.* **35**, 231.
Olivieri, G., and Olivieri, A. (1965). *Mutat. Res.* **2**, 366.
Phillips, D. M. (1970). *J. Cell Biol.* **44**, 243.
Phillips, D. M. (1971). *J. Ultrastruct. Res.* **34**, 567.
Picheral, B. (1972). *Z. Zellforsch. Mikrosk. Anat.* **131**, 399.
Porter, K. R. (1961). In "The Cell" (J. Brachet and A. Mirsky, eds.), Vol. 2, p. 621. Academic Press, New York.
Porter, K. R., and Machado, R. D. (1960). *J. Biophys. Biochem. Cytol.* **7**, 167.
Reger, J. F. (1962). *J. Ultrastruct. Res.* **7**, 550.
Rothschild, Lord. (1955). *Trans. Roy. Entomol. Soc. London* **107**, 289.
Sakai, A., and Shigenaga, M. (1967). *Cytologia* **32**, 72.
Shay, J. W., and Biesele, J. J. (1968). *Cellule* **67**, 269.
Sjöstrand, F. S. (1968). In "Ultrastructure in Biological Systems" (A. J. Dalton and F. Haguenau, eds.), Vol. 4, p. 151. Academic Press, New York.
Stanley, H. P., Bowman, J. T., Romrell, L. J., Reed, S. C., and Wilkinson, R. F. (1972). *J. Ultrastruct. Res.* **41**, 433.
Tokuyasu, K. T. (1974). *Exp. Cell Res.* **84**, 239.
Warner, F. D. (1971). *J. Ultrastruct. Res.* **35**, 210.
Watson, M. L. (1955). *J. Biophys. Biochem. Cytol.* **1**, 257.
Werner, G. (1969). In "Comparative Spermatology" (B. Baccetti, ed.), p. 85.
Werner, G. (1970). In "Morphological Aspects of Andrology" (A. F. Holstein and E. Horstmann, eds.), p. 28.
Whaley, W. G., Kephart, J. E., and Mollenhauer, H. H. (1964). In "Cellular Membranes in Development" (M. Locke, ed.), p. 135. Academic Press, New York.
Whaley, W. G., Dauwalder, M., and Kephart, J. E. (1972). *Science* **182**, 596.
Yasuzumi, G., Fujimura, W., and Ishida, H. (1958). *Exp. Cell Res.* **14**, 268.

CHAPTER 4

PHENOMENA OF CELLULAR RECOGNITION IN SPONGES

G. Van de Vyver

LABORATOIRE DE BIOLOGIE ANIMALE ET CELLULAIRE,
UNIVERSITÉ LIBRE DE BRUXELLES, BRUSSELS, BELGIUM

I. Introduction

When fully grown sponges belonging to the same species are brought into contact, either naturally or by an experimental process, they fuse into a single organism. If they belong to different species, after an initial period of adhesion they "reject" each other by building a nonmerging front, or by moving apart.

In the case of the encrusting sponges *Crambe crambe* and *Ircinia variabilis* or of the freshwater sponges *Ephydatia fluviatilis* and *Spongilla lacustris*, "rejection" can be observed between different strains of a given sponge species (Van de Vyver, 1970). These observations indicate that, despite their very primitive organization sponges are capable of xenogenic and allogenic recognition.

In the absence of any circulatory system, we can assume that the ability for cellular recognition resides in the cell surface and is expressed when cells come into contact. This characteristic of sponges, and the readiness with which sponges can be dissociated into cellular suspension, led to the main experimental work on cellular recognition in these organisms, i.e., studies on the aggregating behavior of dissociated sponge cells.

The technique of cell aggregation is very useful since it allows the mixing of cell suspensions of different kinds and proportions, and because a large number of cells can be brought simultaneously into contact. Two main points were demonstrated by the use of this technique.

1. The aggregation of cells from several species of sponges is rigor-

ously species specific: in interspecific mixtures, the cells of each species immediately recognize each other and aggregate separately (Galstoff, 1925; Moscona, 1963; Humphreys, 1963; McClay, 1974). In the case of other species the dissociated cells are able to build mixed aggregates under certain circumstances (De Laubenfels, 1927; Curtis, 1962, 1970; Sara et al., 1966; Humphreys, 1970a) and later segregate according to species.

2. During their dissociation into single cells, many sponge species release into the medium a soluble factor capable of promoting cell aggregation (cell aggregation factor). For several species, it appears to be a highly species-specific macromolecule (Moscona, 1963, 1968; Humphreys, 1963, 1970b; McClay, 1974; Van de Vyver, 1971a); it is less specific in other species (Humphreys, 1970a; MacLennan and Dodd, 1967).

Purification and characterization of sponge cell aggregating factors was first attempted by Margoliash et al. (1965) in *Microciona prolifera* and *Haliclona occulata*. They found these factors to be protein–carbohydrate complexes. More recently Henkart et al. (1973) have succeeded in determining the chemical nature of the aggregating factor of *Microciona parthena*. This macromolecule is an acidic proteoglycan complex which has, in solution, a molecular weight of several million and contains 47% amino acids and 49% sugars. Its physical properties (Cauldwell et al., 1973) and its configuration, as revealed by the electron microscope (Henkart et al., 1973), indicate a "fibrous" structure with an inner circle and radiating arms. A similar configuration has been observed by Müller and Zahn (1973) for the aggregating factor of *Geodia cydonium*.

An immunological approach to the study of the cell surface and cellular recognition in sponges was followed by Spiegel (1954) and later by MacLennan (1963, 1969, 1970, 1974; Moscona, 1968). MacLennan found that glycopeptides extracted from whole sponges with trichloroacetic acid were antigenic and that they elicited in rabbits precipitating and agglutinating antisera specific for the homologous cells. These results led MacLennan (1969) to conclude that sponge glycopeptides have cell surface specificities. The importance of cell surface constituents in cell specificity has recently been confirmed by Turner and Burger (1973), who demonstrated by the use of lectins the presence of carbohydrates on the cell surface and their involvement in specific cell aggregation.

Most of the experiments dealing with specific sponge aggregation factors support the hypothesis (Moscona, 1963) that the cell aggregating factor acts as a ligand which binds the cells together specifically and consequently plays a key role in selective cell adhesion (Moscona, 1968; MacLennan, 1969; Turner and Burger, 1973).

It is, however, important to stress that a sponge cell aggregate, relative to the normal physiology of the sponge, represents a very special state with respect to the close packing of the cells, their random initial association, and their reorganization into normal sponge structures. These conditions impose restrictions on the usefulness of cell aggregates for deciding if, in sponges, cell adhesion, cell aggregation, and cell recognition represent three aspects of the same phenomenon.

II. Interspecific Recognition

The specificity of cell aggregation in sponges is still a point of controversy; this is probably due in part to differences in the behavior of cells from different sponge species when they are mixed in suspension; and in part to differences in the design of experiments. In some cases, however, the mere mixing of suspensions containing cells from different species has dramatic and irreversible effects on cell adhesiveness and cell viability.

For the experiments to be described here, two marine sponges *Axinella polypoïdes* and *Crambe crambe* have been used. They were collected in the northwestern Mediterranean Sea (Banyuls, France). Because it is difficult to keep these marine sponges in an aquarium (particularly *Crambe*), all the experiments were carried out within a few hours after collection of the organisms.

In monospecific suspensions of mechanically dispersed cells of *Axinella polypoides* and *Crambe crambe*, the cells form aggregates after a few hours at 18°C. But, if cell suspensions from both species are commingled, no aggregation occurs. This loss of cell adhesiveness appears to be stable, since the ability for aggregation is not restored even after several days after rinsing of the cells in Millipore-filtered seawater. A similar behavior is observed when the cells are suspended in a cell-free supernatant of a suspension of cells from another species (Van de Vyver, 1972). The active substance responsible for this inhibition appears to be a heat-labile macromolecule with molecular weight above 10,000. Its inhibitory effect is proportional to its concentration (see Table I). In the absence of any knowledge of the chemical nature of the substance, we shall define 1 unit of this inhibition factor as the quantity released by the dissociation of 10^5 cells in 1 ml of seawater.

The inhibitory effects of a cell-free supernatant obtained from *Crambe*, on the aggregation of *Axinella* cells is much more severe than those in the reverse situation. In fact, there is considerable cell lysis in this combination. Indeed, using a similar concentration of inhibition factor (500 U per 10^8 cells suspended in 1 ml), more than 50% of *Axinella* cells are lysed by the *Crambe* factor, while in the reverse situation *Crambe* cells only become motionless. In 1929 Galtsoff pointed out that

G. VAN DE VYVER

TABLE I

AGGREGATING BEHAVIOR OF *Axinella* CELLS IN
PRESENCE OF DIFFERENT CONCENTRATIONS
OF *Crambe* INHIBITING FACTOR

Axinella suspension	Units of *Crambe* inhibition factor	Aggregating behavior
10^8 cells in 1 ml	3000	−
	1000	−
	500	−
	250	±
	125	±
	75	+

the movement of archeocytes of one species of sponge is inhibited by the presence of cells from another species, and consequently that cell aggregation was inhibited in such combinations; his assumption was that motility of archeocytes was essential for cell reaggregation and tissue reconstruction. He called the phenomenon "heteroagglutination." In a recent paper, studying the specificity of factors produced by five marine sponges, McClay (1974) described such inhibitory effects in several combinations of cells from different species of sponges. In the case of one of these species, *Haliclona viridis*, he succeeded in separating the cell-aggregation enhancing activity from the inhibiting activity by gel filtration on Sephadex G-100.

Several species of sponges, and in particular the genus *Axinella*, produce human blood hemagglutinins (Bretting, 1973; Bretting and Renwrantz, 1973; Gold et al., 1974). We have checked whether these agglutinins are related to the inhibitory effects on sponge cell aggregation in heterospecific mixtures. The technique consisted of mixing in a hemagglutination dish a few drops of a cell suspension (10^8 cell/ml) or of a cell-free supernatant from dissociated cells with a few drops of a human erythrocyte suspension (2×10^9 cells/ml) and checking for agglutination of erythrocytes. The results are given in Table II. Under these experimental conditions, only the cells of *Axinella polypoïdes* showed hemagglutination activity. In contrast to the cell suspension, the dissociation supernatant, centrifuged at 40,000 *g* for 30 minutes, was completely devoid of activity. For *Crambe*, both the cellular suspension and the supernatant were inactive. The absence of hemagglutinating activity in the *Axinella* and *Crambe* supernatants, both of which strongly inhibit cross-species cell aggregation, indicates that the hemagglutinins (of *Axinella*, at least) are not involved in the latter effect.

Therefore, it appears that some sponges produce substances that are

TABLE II

HUMAN BLOOD AGGLUTINATION BY *Axinella* AND *Crambe*

Sample	A₁	A₂	B	O
Axinella				
Squash in NaCl 0.9%	+	+	+	+
Cellular suspension in sea water	+	+	+	+
Supernatant of dissociated cells	−	−	−	−
Crambe				
Squash in NaCl 0.9%	−	−	−	−
Cellular suspension in sea water	−	−	−	−
Supernatant of dissociated cells	−	−	−	−

lytic for foreign sponge cells, as reported by Galtsoff (1929) and myself, and that these substances represent a kind of cell "recognition" which is completely independent from morphogenetic cell aggregation and normal cell adhesion.

III. Intraspecific Recognition

A. TECHNICAL DATA

1. *Culture Techniques*

For the experiments dealing with intraspecific recognition, three strains, alpha, beta, and delta of the freshwater sponge *Ephydatia fluviatilis* have been used.

At the end of the seasonal growth, this sponge produces asexual reproductive bodies called gemmules. These contain certain specialized cells encysted in a hard shell. In spring, the gemmules hatch, the cells multiply, emerge, and differentiate to construct a sponge (Rasmont, 1975). Cells derived from different gemmules may or may not merge into a single sponge, depending on whether they belong to the same strain. Thus, a strain is defined as that population of a sponge whose gemmules are able to form a single functional individual when they hatch in close proximity (Van de Vyver, 1970). The different strains identified so far (more than twelve are known for the vicinity of Brussels) all appear very similar by their morphological characteristics, but very different by their physiological properties (Figs. 1 and 2).

In these experiments, gemmules of appropriate strains (stored at 0°C until use) were placed in petri dishes and incubated at 20°C in M medium (Rasmont, 1961). A more complete description of the culture techniques is given by Rasmont (1961, 1963, 1975). For consistency, sponges derived

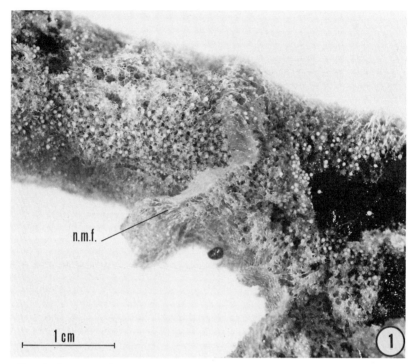

FIG. 1. A nonmerging front (n.m.f.) between two sponges belonging to different strains of the freshwater sponge *Ephydatia fluviatilis*, grown in the field. Photograph by courtesy of Ph. Willenz.

from gemmules were used for experiments always 8 days after the beginning of incubation. At the end of this period, the young sponges were fully differentiated. Usually, sponges derived from batches of ten gemmules of the same strain were used. A ten-gemmule sponge, 8 days old, contains about 10^6 cells; it includes the discarded cases of the gemmules from which the founding cells had emerged.

2. Cell Dissociation and Factor Extraction

To prepare cellular suspensions, 8-day sponges are scraped from the culture dishes and transferred into the dispersion medium. This medium, referred to as CMF (Ca^{2+}, Mg^{2+} free), contains the following components (milliequivalents per liter): Na^+, 1.00; K^+, 0.05; SiO_3^{2-}, 0.50; HCO_3^-, 0.50; Cl^-, 0.05. Within the medium, the cells are mechanically dispersed by gentle pipetting. After 15 minutes, the gemmule cases are removed and the cellular suspension is centrifuged at 200 g for 5 minutes. The pellet is washed twice in CMF and then resuspended in the appropriate medium.

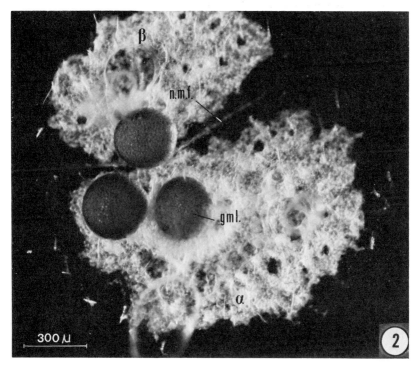

FIG. 2. Nonmerging front between two sponges of different strains cultivated under laboratory conditions. The sponge above is built from one gemmule (gml) belonging to the strain beta; the one below is built from two gemmules belonging to the strain alpha.

To prepare aggregation factor, the sponge is mechanically dispersed in CMF at 20°C. After 15 minutes the cells are removed by centrifugation and the supernatant is filtered through a Millipore filter. This supernatant is used as the *Ephydatia* aggregation factor. In the absence of accurate knowledge of the chemical nature of this factor, 1 unit is defined arbitrarily as the quantity of factor released by 10^5 cells in 1 ml of CMF.

3. Measurement of Cell Adhesiveness

Cell adhesiveness has been measured by the technique proposed by Curtis (1969). It consists of determining the number of cells in suspension, which, when subjected to a laminar shear flow, form adhesions as they collide. To obtain a laminar shear flow, a Couette viscosimeter has been used. A detailed description of the method is given by Curtis (1969, 1970, 1973).

Briefly, the viscosimeter consists of two coaxial cylinders: the internal is fixed while the external rotates with a known velocity. The cell suspension is poured between the cylinders. Movement of the external cylinder subjects the cell suspension to a laminar shear flow. In such a flow, successive layers of liquid slowly slide over each other. A cell in one of these layers will thus move with respect to the cells in neighboring layers and will eventually collide with them whenever the two cells lie on streamlines less than one cell diameter apart. This mechanism would cause the rate of collision between cells to be proportional to the shear rate. After collision, the cells will adhere if their adhesive strength exceeds the shear forces. The probability of adhesion (collision efficiency), which is directly related to the cell adhesiveness, can be measured by comparing the observed decrease in the number of collisions calculated from the shear rate. Even in the absence of shear flow, Brownian motion alone would also cause some collisions between cells. However, in our experiments, the shear rate was large enough to make the brownian contribution negligible. In practice, 1–2 ml of a suspension of cells poured into the viscosimeter were subjected to shear rates between 8 and 10 sec^{-1} at room temperature. Samples were collected every 5 minutes for half an hour. The number of particles per unit volume was counted with a hemacytometer and the collision efficiency (α) was evaluated using the relation derived by Swift and Friedlander (1964) for colloidal particles.

$$N_t = N_o e^{-4/\pi G\alpha\phi t}$$

where N_o and N_t are the total number of particles of all sizes at the start of aggregation and at time t, respectively; G is the shear rate; ϕ is the total volume of the cells.

B. Results

1. Ephydatia fluviatilis as a Material for the Study of Cell Recognition

Freshwater sponges lend themselves well to studies on phenomena of cellular recognition. *Ephydatia fluviatilis* can be propagated under laboratory conditions. The only requisite is to start the cultures from gemmules, not from fully grown sponges collected in the field.

Sponges grown from gemmules under controlled conditions can be kept alive for 2 or 3 months, especially if they are regularly fed with dead bacteria (Rasmont, 1963). Such cultures provide physiologically and chronologically standardized material. Aging is a very important factor with respect to phenomena of cellular recognition, because the proportion of differentiated and undifferentiated cells varies greatly with the age of the organism and this has a significant bearing on the rate of cell aggregation. Cells from young sponges which are rich in undifferentiated cells (essentially archeocytes) aggregate more readily and faster than older cells.

Another interesting and useful aspect of the biology of *Ephydatia fluviatilis* is the existence of definite and permanent strains, genetically stable throughout asexual and sexual reproduction (Van de Vyver 1970; Van de Vyver and Willenz, 1975). Until very recently it was not possible to distinguish between individual sponges by morphological criteria (Borojevic *et al.*, 1967); this has led those who study these organisms to consider them in terms of species, rather than in terms of individuals within a given species. The results obtained with *Ephydatia fluviatilis* lead us to be very cautious about this generalization. Indeed, all the experiments dealing with the physiology of this sponge, and particularly with cellular recognition, show significant behavioral differences between the strains (Mawet and Rasmont, 1971; Rasmont, 1974; Curtis and Van de Vyver, 1971; Van de Vyver and Willenz, 1975). Finally, it is noteworthy that while most sponges are able to build aggregates from cellular suspensions, only in a few cases has it been possible to obtain functional sponges from the aggregates under laboratory conditions. Dissociated cells of *Ephydatia fluviatilis* reconstitute differentiated sponges after 1–3 days, depending on the strain (Brien, 1937; Van de Vyver, 1971a). This ability is of special usefulness for detecting late segregation of cells.

2. Observations

In mixed suspensions of cells from the alpha and delta strain of *Ephydatia*, we obtain composite aggregates in a few hours. These composite aggregates can subsist for several days, after which segregation takes place. In fact, the segregation occurs always just before the aggregates settle down and spread out on the floor of the culture dish. We have investigated the processes that might be responsible for that late segregation and in particular, if the cell aggregation factor plays a role.

Under standardized conditions of medium, cell concentration, and temperature, the aggregation rate of cells of a given strain in homogeneous suspension depends upon the concentration of the homologous aggregation factor. A dose-response curve established for the strains alpha and delta with the Couette viscosimeter using a cell concentration of about 10^6/ml at 20°C clearly points this out (Fig. 3) (Curtis and Van de Vyver 1971). The aggregation factor of *Ephydatia fluviatilis* is inactive at low temperatures (4°C), but at room temperature it promotes cell clustering also in the absence of Ca^{2+}. However, in the latter situation, the cell clusters never develop into functional sponges. The *Ephydatia* factor is a thermolabile substance. Preliminary results sug-

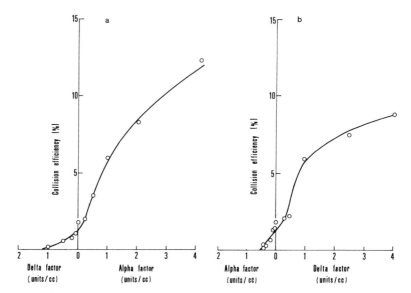

FIG. 3. Dose-response curves for the adhesiveness of *Ephydatia* alpha strain cells (a) and delta strain cells (b) in the presence of homologous and heterologous factors. After Curtis and Van de Vyver (1971).

gest that its molecular weight is around 50,000 (De Sutter, personal communication).

The activity of aggregation factor prepared from one strain was tested on other strains. The evidence that cells of different strains can form mixed aggregates led us to expect that their aggregation factors might not be strain specific. However, measurements of cell adhesiveness showed that the aggregation factors enhanced only the mutual adhesiveness of homologous cells. Moreover, a factor derived from one strain reduced the adhesiveness of cells belonging to other strains (Fig. 3). This is the case if the factor acts in presence of Ca^{2+}, whereas in the absence of Ca^{2+} the factor loses its specificity.

The inhibitory effect of heterologous factors on cell aggregation could explain some aspects of cell recognition. We know that fully grown sponges belonging to different strains move away from each other when brought into contact. Likewise, in mixed aggregates the cells from different strains sort out before the reconstitution of functional sponges.

Since the factor can behave like a diffusible molecule and is probably produced by all the cells of a sponge, its concentration is probably maximal within the sponge body, and minimal at the periphery. Therefore, adhesiveness of cells at the periphery might be lower. When two sponges of identical strain come into contact, the concentration of factor will gradually rise in the contact region and will increase cell adhesiveness there, thus facilitating formation of a single sponge body. On the other hand, when sponges of different strains make contact, there is initial adhesion; however, as the concentration of the factors presumably increases in the contact zone, the cells separate. One might speculate that the heterologous factors progressively reduce adhesiveness between the heterologous cells, so that cells of different strains become unable to adhere to each other, and the two sponges separate.

In the case of cellular suspensions derived from different strains of *Ephydatia*, the inhibitory effects of the heterologous factors on cell adhesiveness appear to be reversible. In fact, if the cells are maintained under favorable conditions, they soon begin to aggregate even in the presence of a heterologous factor.

Experiments performed by Moscona (1968) with cells of the marine sponges *Microciona prolifera* and *Haliclona occulata* showed that aggregation of the cells in the presence of the homologous aggregation factor is accompanied by removal of factor from the medium due to association of the factor with the cells. Similar results were obtained by De Sutter with *Ephydatia* (personal communication). Therefore the reversibility of the inhibitory effect of the strain-specific heterologous factors on cell aggregation in *Ephydatia* could be due to a rapid turnover of the cell membrane and a high rate of synthesis of the homologous factor.

Measurements of cell adhesiveness recorded with the viscosimeter in the presence of homologous factor confirm that the factor plays a key role in cell adhesion, since cell adhesiveness increases proportionately with factor concentration. The inhibiting activity of heterologous factors suggests that the factor acts as a cell ligand and that it may also modulate the specificity of cell adhesion through quantitative effects.

IV. Cell Type Specificity

It was of interest to determine whether the different cell types which constitute a single sponge individual are able to recognize each other after their dissociation and if they sort out in aggregates according to type. To study this, we have examined (using the electron microscope) the development of aggregates formed in a cell suspension of *Ephydatia fluviatilis*, strain delta. This strain is particularly convenient for such study because its cells make minute aggregates (100 μm) which can be readily examined with the electron microscope, and which become organized into typical sponge structures within 24 hours.

Using histological techniques Brien (1937) demonstrated for *Ephydatia fluviatilis* that the various differentiated cells which recombine into aggregates retain their characteristic differentiation as the aggregates

develop into functional sponges. He found that, after the initial aggregation phase during which the cells adhere randomly, they move about and
gradually segregate and sort out according to types in their appropriate
positions. Thus, during this second phase, cells of the same type associate
into the kinds of structures from which they were derived in the original
sponge. This is easy to follow for, at least, one cell type, the choanocytes.

Choanocytes have a typical morphology characterized by a flagellum
and an apical collar formed by a large number of fibrils (Rasmont *et
al.*, 1957; Fjerdingstad, 1961). In the sponge, these cells form choanocyte
chambers. During the first 5 hours of aggregation, the choanocytes are
found randomly dispersed in the aggregates and many show pinocytotic
activity (Fig. 4). As the aggregates increase in size, the choanocytes send
out filopodia typical of migrating cells and they assemble into clusters
of three or four cells. Twenty hours later, no individual choanocytes are
seen within the aggregates, all having been assembled into typical choanocyte chambers (Fig. 5).

It would be of interest to follow in detail the behavior and fate of
other cell types throughout the development of aggregates. Judging from
the behavior of the choanocytes, it appears that the organization of a
functional sponge from a cellular suspension represents, at least largely
a morphogenetic process during which cells belonging to the same histological type recognize each other and reassemble into characteristic structures. At present, nothing is known about the mechanisms which are involved in cell type specificity in sponges; the random initial adhesion
of cells followed by their subsequent sorting out suggests that different
cell kinds of interactions may be involved at different stages of the reaggregation sequence.

V. Discussion

The relatively simple structure of the sponge body may account for
the ability of sponges belonging to the same species and strain to fuse
into a single organism. This extraordinary capacity is clearly evidenced
by the possibility of exchange-grafting tissues between adult sponges of
the same species (Moscona, 1968) and by the fact that sponges hatched
from numerous gemmules can fuse into one functional organism. Until
recently, it was not possible to study individual differences within a given
sponge species (Borojevic *et al.*, 1967). Experiments based on the culture
of gemmules (Rasmont, 1956; Van de Vyver 1970) or on cell aggregation
(Van de Vyver, 1971a,b) have demonstrated, at least for some freshwater
sponges, a form of intraspecific recognition, that we have called strain
specificity. Thus, despite their low level of morphological organization,
sponges display species and strain specificities. Moreover, the different

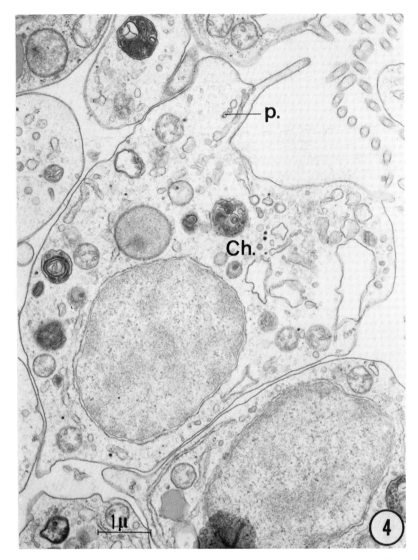

FIG. 4. One choanocyte (Ch.) isolated in a 5-hour aggregate. The cell shows small pinosomes (p.).

cell types involved in one sponge body apparently display type specificities.

In a recent paper dealing with "self" vs "not self" recognition in sponges, MacLennan (1974) discussed the roles of glycopeptides, aggregation factors, and heteroagglutinins. He stressed for the glycopeptides

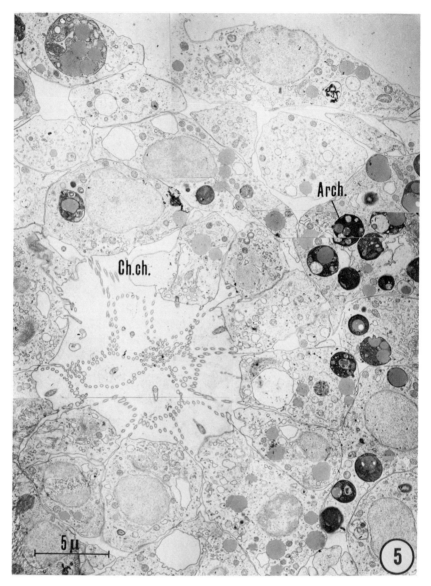

Fig. 5. In a 20-hour aggregate, the choanocytes are gathered again into typical choanocyte chambers (Ch. ch.).

(MacLennan, 1970, 1974) the common serological specificities with the cell surface, attributable to related structural features. The aggregation factors are protein–carbohydrates complexes derived from the cell surface which can selectively enhance aggregation of cells from homologous species and appear to play a key role in morphogenetic cell adhesion (Moscona, 1963, 1968; Humphreys, 1963; MacLennan and Dodd, 1967; McClay, 1974; Van de Vyver, 1971a; Curtis and Van de Vyver, 1971). Turner and Burger (1973) and Turner *et al.* (1974) suggested that the specific interaction between the cell surface and the aggregation factor may involve the recognition of a specific carbohydrate on the factor by receptors of the cell surfaces which can be extracted by a dilute salt solution. The existence of specific membrane receptors which play a role in cell adhesion has been demonstrated by Beug *et al.* (1973) for slime molds. The authors prepared univalent antibodies against the membrane of aggregation-competent cells and showed that these antibodies inhibited cell adhesion. Finally, the heteroagglutinins and lytic substances produced by sponges exert species-specific effects in sponges.

The existence of these substances offers tentative explanations concerning recognition of "self" vs "not self"; they suggest that morphogenetic cell aggregation and selective cell adhesion are closely related phenomena, at least in those cases when cell contact specificity is displayed early in the process of cell aggregation.

The formation of mixed aggregates of sponge cells from different species or from different strains which later undergo sorting out is not clearly understood. Such aggregates have been rarely observed in mixtures of cells from different marine sponge species (De Laubenfels, 1927; Curtis, 1962; Sara *et al.*, 1966), and their existence was denied by Humphreys (1970b). Yet this phenomenon appears to be common for aggregation of heterotypic embryonic vertebrate cells (Holtfreter, 1944; Moscona and Moscona, 1952; Moscona, 1965; Steinberg, 1964). Working with two cell types able to form heterotypic aggregates (liver and neural retina cells) when they are commingled in cellular suspension, Roth and Weston (1967) observed that cells collected by preformed aggregates preferentially make adhesion with homotypic aggregates. They attributed the specificity in their experimental system to the recovery of the cell membrane from the despecifying effects of trypsin dissociation. This explanation is difficult to accept for sponge cells and for amphibian embryonic cells (Holtfreter, 1944) since they are mechanically dissociated. Indeed, since a sponge resembles more a society of individual cells than a true metazoon, the injury to individual cell introduced by dissociation is probably limited.

The differential cell adhesivity hypothesis promoted by Steinberg (1964) is also difficult to apply to sponge cells because of the species and strain specificities displayed in sponge cell aggregation. This means that what used to be considered as a homogeneous sponge suspension, according to species or strain, is in fact a heterogeneous mixture of several cell types. At the present time, very little is known about cell type specificity in sponges, although John *et al.* (1971) pointed out the unequal aggregative ability of the different cell types separated on a Ficoll gradient. This behavior makes the hypothesis of differential cell adhesiveness inadequate for explaining sorting out in this system.

The evidence discussed in this paper concerning sorting out of sponge cells in interstrain mixtures led to another hypothesis (Curtis and Van de Vyver, 1971) based on the effects of aggregation factors. These authors suggested that a homologous aggregation factor increases cell adhesiveness while a heterologous factor decreases cell adhesiveness, the latter resulting from a competitive saturation of cell membrane receptors.

VI. Summary

Some phenomena involved in sponge cell recognition were investigated during the reaggregation of dissociated cells. It was pointed out that in sponges cell recognition occurs at three levels; cell type specificity, intraspecific recognition, and interspecific recognition.

The sponges used for the experiments dealing with cell type specificity and intraspecific recognition belong to several strains of the fresh-water sponge: *Ephydatia fluviatilis*. Those used for the experiments dealing with interspecific recognition belong to two marine species *Axinella polypoïdes* and *Crambe crambe*. The behavior of the reaggregating cells was followed under the microscope and their adhesiveness was measured using a Couette viscosimeter. In these experiments, the incompatibility is expressed in terms of variability of cell adhesiveness. For *E. fluviatilis*, the adhesiveness of a given strain depends upon the concentration of a strain specific aggregation factor. This factor increases the adhesiveness of homologous cells although it decreases the adhesiveness of cells belonging to other strains.

Similar results were obtained between the two species of marine sponges. In presence of a soluble macromolecule released in the dissociation medium of one species the adhesivity of cells which belong to the other species falls nearly to zero.

REFERENCES

Beug, H., Katz, F. E., and Gerisch, G. (1973). *J. Cell Biol.* **56,** 647.
Borojevic, R., Fry, W. G., Jones, W. C., Levi, C., Rasmont, R., Sara, M., and Vacelet, J. (1967). *Bull. Mus. Hist. Natur., Paris* [3] **39,** 1224.
Bretting, H. (1973). *Z. Immunitaets forsch., Exp. Klin. Immunol.* **146,** 239.
Bretting, H., and Renwrantz, L. (1973). *Z. Immunitaets forsch., Exp. Klin. Immunol.* **145,** 242.
Brien, P. (1937). *Arch. Biol.* **48,** 185.
Cauldwel, C. B., Henkart, P., and Humphreys, T. (1973). *Biochemistry* **12,** 3051.

Curtis, A. S. G. (1962). *Nature* (*London*) **196**, 245.
Curtis, A. S. G. (1969). *J. Embryol. Exp. Morphol.* **22**, 305.
Curtis, A. S. G. (1970). *Symp. Zool. Soc. London* **25**.
Curtis, A. S. G. (1973). *Progr. Biophys. Mol. Biol.* **27**, 317.
Curtis, A. S. G., and Hocking, L. M. (1970). *Trans. Faraday Soc.* **66**, 1381.
Curtis, A. S. G., and Van de Vyver, G. (1971). *J. Embryol. Exp. Morphol.* **26**, 295.
De Laubenfels, M. W. (1927). *Carnegie Inst. Wash., Yearb.* **26**, 219.
De Vos, L. (1971). *J. Microsc.* (*Paris*) **10**, 283.
Fjerdingstad, E. J. (1961). *Z.* **53**, 645.
Galtsoff, P. (1925). *J. Exp. Zool.* **42**, 183.
Galtsoff, P. (1929). *Biol. Bull.* **57**, 250.
Gold, E. R., Phelps, C. F., Khalap, S., and Balding, P. (1974). *Ann. N.Y. Acad. Sci.* **234**, 122.
Henkart, P., Humphreys, S., and Humphreys, T. (1973). *Biochemistry* **12**, 3045.
Holtfreter, J. (1944). *Rev. Can. Biol.* **3**, 220.
Humphreys, T. (1963). *Develop. Biol.* **8**, 27.
Humphreys, T. (1970a). *Symp. Zool. Soc. London* **25**.
Humphreys, T. (1970b). *Nature* (*London*) **228**, 685.
John, H. A., Campo, M. S., Mackenzie, A. M., and Kemp, R. B. (1971). *Nature* (*London*), *New Biol.* **230**, 126.
Leveaux, M. (1939). *Ann. Soc. Roy. Zool. Belg.* **70**, 53.
McClay, D. (1971). *Biol. Bull.* **141**, 319.
McClay, D. (1974). *J. Exp. Zool.* **188**, 89.
MacLennan, A. P. (1963). *Biochemistry* **89**, 99.
MacLennan, A. P. (1969). *J. Exp. Zool.* **172**, 253.
MacLennan, A. P. (1970). *Symp. Zool. Soc. London* **25**.
MacLennan, A. P. (1974). *Arch. Biol.* **85**, 53.
MacLennan, A. P., and Dodd, R. Y. (1967). *J. Embryol. Exp. Morphol.* **17**, 474.
Margoliash, E., Schenck, J. R., Hargie, M. P., Burokas, S., Richter, W. R., Barlow, G. H., and Moscona, A. A. (1965). *Biochem. Biophys. Res. Commun.* **20**, 383.
Mawet, A., and Rasmont, R. (1971). *Arch. Biol.* **82**, 543.
Moscona, A. A. (1963). *Proc. Nat. Acad. Sci. U.S.* **49**, 742.
Moscona, A. A. (1965). *In* "Cells and Tissues in Culture" (E. N. Willmer, ed.), Vol. 1, p. 489. Academic Press, New York.
Moscona, A. A. (1968). *Develop. Biol.* **18**, 250.
Moscona, A. A., and Moscona, M. H. (1952). *J. Anat.* **86**, 287.
Muller, W. E., and Zahn, R. K. (1973). *Exp. Cell Res.* **80**, 95.
Rasmont, R. (1956). *Ann. Soc. Roy. Zool. Belg.* **86**, 349.
Rasmont, R. (1961). *Ann. Soc. Roy. Zool. Belg.* **91**, 147.
Rasmont, R. (1963). *Develop. Biol.* **8**, 243.
Rasmont, R. (1974). *Experientia* **30**, 792.
Rasmont, R. (1975). *Curr. Top. Develop. Biol.* **10**, (in press).
Rasmont, R., Bouillon, J., Castiaux, P., and Vandermeersche, G. (1957). *C. R. Acad. Sci.* **245**, 1571.
Roth, S. A., and Weston, J. A. (1967). *Proc. Nat. Acad. Sci. U.S.* **58**, 974.
Sara, M. (1968). *Acta Embryol. Morphol. Exp.* **10**, 228.
Sara, M., Liaci, L., and Melone, N. (1966). *Nature* (*London*) **210**, 1167.
Spiegel, M. (1954). *Biol. Bull.* **107**, 130.
Steinberg, M. S. (1964). *In* "Cellular Membranes in Development" (M. Locke, ed.). Academic Press, New York.

Swift, D. L., and Friedlander, S. K. (1964). *J. Colloid Sci.* **19**, 621.

Turner, R. S., and Burger, M. M. (1973). *Nature (London)* **244**, 509.

Turner, R. S., Weinbaum, G., Kuhns, W. J., and Burger, M. M. (1974). *Arch. Biol.* **85**, 35.

Van de Vyver, G. (1970). *Ann. Embryol. Morphol.* **3**, 251.

Van de Vyver, G. (1971a). *Ann. Embryol. Morphol.* **4**, 373.

Van de Vyver, G. (1971b). *Arch. Zool. Exp. Gen.* **112**, 55.

Van de Vyver, G. (1972). *In* "Phylogenic and Ontogenic Study of the Immune Response and its Contribution to the Immunological Theory," Colloque INSERM 1972.

Van de Vyver, G., and Willenz, P. (1975). *Wilhelm Roux' Arch. Entwicklungsmech. Organismen* **177**, 41.

Weinbaum, G., and Burger, M. (1973). *Nature (London)* **244**, 210.

CHAPTER 5

FRESHWATER SPONGES AS A MATERIAL FOR THE STUDY OF CELL DIFFERENTIATION*

R. Rasmont

LABORATOIRE DE BIOLOGIE ANIMALE ET CELLULAIRE,
UNIVERSITÉ LIBRE DE BRUXELLES, BRUSSELS, BELGIUM

I. Introduction

To students in cell biology sponges are especially well known for the ability of their cells to reaggregate, after having been experimentally dissociated into cell suspensions, and eventually to resume a functional organization. Our purpose is to show that, besides their usefulness for this type of experimental work, sponges are a suitable material for studying cell-to-cell interactions in the course of their normal development, and that this aspect deserves more attention than it has so far received.

To be suitable for developmental biology studies, an organism should

* Dedicated to the memory of Paul Brien.

141

be able to undergo its normal development *in vitro*. It is very difficult to cultivate and propagate marine sponges, even in a seaside laboratory, particularly for several years in a row. On the other hand, freshwater sponges reproduce asexually by producing gemmules (groups of embryonic cells enclosed in a hard shell); this mode of "somatic" reproduction makes it possible to obtain "clonal" cultures, in the laboratory (Rasmont, 1961, 1963) as well as in the field (Van de Vyver, 1970). Not only do gemmules provide us with a means of conveniently starting cultures of sponges, but the formation of the gemmules within the sponge and the hatching of a gemmule and its development into an organism are, by themselves, developmental processes that are worthy of study.

Although in the present review we shall concentrate on the physiological aspects of the asexual reproduction of freshwater sponges, the morphological features of the process are probably not familiar to many biologists and deserve to be briefly described.

The general anatomy of freshwater sponges is described in textbooks (Hyman, 1940). However, it should be stressed that the histological organization of these animals is far from being as stable as that of higher metazoa. Time-lapse cinematography of "sandwich cultures" of sponges (see Section II, D) makes it clear that every structure, even choanocyte chambers and spicules, is very mobile. A live sponge is more in the nature of a dynamic society of individual cells than a stable tissue organization.

A. DEFINITION OF CELL TYPES AND ANATOMICAL FEATURES

A few anatomical and cytological definitions concerning especially freshwater sponges will facilitate our account.

The *choanocytes*, or collar cells, are small cells, approximately 5 μm in diameter, bearing a flagellum surrounded by a collarlike palisade of cytoplasmic microvilli. They are grouped in spherical *chambers* irrigated and drained by an *aquiferous system*.

The *pinacocytes* are flat cells that constitute an endothelium-like layer (the *pinacoderm*) on all the surfaces of the sponge that are in contact either with the water or with the solid substratum to which the sponge is attached.

The *mesohyl* is that part of the sponge that extends between the pinacoderm and the choanocyte chambers. It contains various forms of amoeboid cells.

The *lophocytes* are particular amoeboid cells, responsible for the secretion of a collagen network through the mesohyl.

The *scleroblasts* are amoeboid cells that secrete the skeletal spicules (in this case siliceous); the *spongocytes* secrete spongin, i.e., a special form of collagen.

The *trophocytes* are amoeboid cells, rich with glycogen and lipids, that take part in the vitellogenesis (formation and storage of yolk). The *archaeocytes* are amoeboid cells rich in primary and secondary lysosomes; they function as the digestive cells in the sponge. Moreover, they are the stem cells in oogenesis and in the formation of gemmules. When the gemmule hatches, these cells are able to differentiate into any other cell type. As a working hypothesis, we shall assume that the archaeocytes retain this capability also in the adult sponge.

In these definitions and in the following descriptions, we follow the terminology of Borojevic *et al.* (1968).

B. FORMATION OF THE GEMMULE

Most of our knowledge about the formation of a gemmule derives from histological and cytological studies, either with the light microscope (Leveaux, 1939; Rasmont, 1956) or with the electron microscope (De Vos, 1971, 1972). It is also possible, to stimulate sponges in "sandwich-type" cultures into gemmulation by treating them with theophylline (Rasmont, 1974) and to follow the phenomenon by means of time-lapse cinematography (Rasmont and De Vos, 1974).

The first noticeable event in the formation of a gemmule is the aggregation, in a hitherto undistinguishable area of the mesohyl of two kinds of amoeboid cells, archaeocytes and trophocytes. As soon as they come in contact, the former phagocytose the latter. The ensuing *phagosomes*, containing large fragments of trophocytes, are later transformed into vitelline platelets. These platelets contain more or less distinct remnants of the organelles of the engulfed trophocytes (Ruthmann, 1965; Simons and Müller, 1966; De Vos, 1971).

The last amoeboid cells that join the cell aggregate are spongocytes. They stay at the surface of the aggregate, gradually surrounding it with a single layer of epithelium. This epithelium secretes several layers of differently arranged collagen fibers. While it does so, microscleres (a special form of small spicules) that have been secreted elsewhere in the mesohyl, are carried to the growing shell and embedded in it (De Vos, 1972). The form of the spicules and the structure of the shell vary according to the species or even the strain. In every case however, there is a small circular spot, the micropyle, where the hull remains thin (De Vos and Rozenfeld, 1974).

By the time the shell is completed, all the trophocytes have been absorbed by the archaeocytes and transformed into yolk. The last morphological events to take place are the disappearance of the glycogen from the vitelline platelets (De Vos, 1971) and a karyokinesis that renders the cells binucleated (Leveaux, 1939; De Vos, 1971). In this final state the archaeocytes of the gemmule are generally referred to as *thesocytes*. The number of cells in one gemmule ranges from several hundreds to several thousands.

C. HATCHING OF THE GEMMULE

In the resting gemmule, the two nuclei of each thesocyte lie in close contact. The first indication of hatching in a gemmule is that the nuclei move apart in most of its cells (Berthold, 1969). At 20°C, this occurs during the first day of incubation (Rozenfeld, 1970).

During the following 24 hours, the thesocytes undergo nuclear and cytoplasmic divisions, some of them passing through a four-nucleated stage, all of them ultimately becoming smaller archaeocytes with a single nucleus. Some of these archaeocytes undergo a further change; they become elongated, digest their vitelline platelets and lose their nucleolus. The resulting cell type is a *histoblast* (Brien, 1932; Berthold, 1969; Rozenfeld, 1970; Schmidt, 1970). These transformations occur in an orderly way, so as to give rise to a gradient, the histoblasts being more numerous toward the micropyle. The opening of the latter is probably due to the local digestion of the shell by the histoblasts (Rozenfeld, 1971). It is intriguing that these cells begin to secrete extracellular collagen fibers even before leaving the open shell of the gemmule (L. De Vos, unpublished).

The first histoblasts that migrate out of the shell, onto its external surface and onto the substrate, differentiate into a pinacodermal envelope. All the other cells migrate through the micropyle into this space. By that time, their characteristics range from archaeocytes to histoblasts, depending on the state of their nucleus and the extent to which their yolk has already been digested (L. De Vos, unpublished).

The secretion of the first spicules occurs very soon thereafter (Brien, 1932). With the electron microscope, scleroblasts can be distinguished from archaeocytes only by the presence of the incipient spicule in the former (L. De Vos, unpublished).

The choanocyte chambers appear a few hours later, first as clusters of choanoblasts. Each cluster is the result of repeated divisions of a single archaeocyte (Brien, 1932; Wintermann, 1951).

D. THE PHYSIOLOGICAL PROBLEMS OF GEMMULATION

The physiological problems of asexual reproduction in sponges are the classical problems of developmental biology:

1. What causes four types of cells to aggregate into a gemmule-forming cluster? What factors influence their differentiation into the specialized structures of a gemmule?

2. What keeps a gemmule from hatching immediately after having been completed?

3. How is the differentiation of the cells coordinated, and what are the morphogenetic processes which lead to the development of the gemmule into a sponge?

II. Culture Techniques

We shall deal briefly only with the more general techniques used in most of our experimental work.

A. COLLECTION AND STORAGE OF GEMMULES

As we do not yet have a technique for the bulk production of gemmules in the laboratory, we depend for our stocks on gemmules collected from sponges growing in the field. Four species grow in the ponds and brooks near Brussels. We have occasionally worked on each of them, but mostly on *Ephydatia fluviatilis*. In this species, we have recognized the existence of several strains, with different physiological properties (Rasmont, 1970; Van de Vyver, 1970).

One cannot depend on "wild" sponges for the collection of stock gemmules intended for physiological work because it is very difficult to avoid interstrain or possibly even interspecies contamination. For several years now, we have avoided this difficulty by cultivating pure strains of sponges started from gemmules on glass plates submersed in ponds.

In the autumn, when the sponges are crammed with gemmules, they are harvested. The gemmules are easily isolated, washed, and stored in water at 0°C. Before any experimental use, the gemmules are cleansed with dilute hydrogen peroxide (Rasmont, 1961). Stored in this way, the gemmules retain their ability to germinate for years. However, some of their properties, e.g., their hatching speed, or the readiness of the ensuing sponge to gemmulate, undergo a slow change with time. This is important in evaluating results from experiments made with gemmules of different ages.

B. CULTURE MEDIA

Several authors have devised culture media for freshwater sponges (Jørgensen, 1944; Rasmont, 1961; Strekal and McDiffett, 1974). All these media are very dilute solutions of a few ions: Na^+, K^+, Ca^{2+}, Mg^{2+}, Cl^-, HCO_3^-, SO_4^{2-} and SiO_3^{2-}. The optimum concentration and ionic balance appear to be somewhat different from one species to another.

C. CULTURES IN PETRI DISHES

Gemmules cleaned with H_2O_2 can easily be made to germinate in petri dishes with culture medium; provided they are not in diapause (developmental arrest), they hatch at room temperature in 3–5 days. When two or more gemmules of the same species and strain are deposited side by side in the dish, the sponges resulting from their germination merge into a single individual. Indeed, the definition of strain similarity in sponges is based on the occurrence of such a merger (Rasmont, 1970; Van de Vyver, 1970).

The gemmules can be arranged in a definite array of clusters in the petri dish: this way, one obtains sponges that are, from their beginning, of definite sizes. For many experiments, it is convenient to use 120 gemmules per 25-ml dish. This number has many divisors so that the same total biomass can be subdivided into diverse fractions.

D. Sandwich Cultures

Ankel and Eigenbrodt (1950) have shown that sponges are able to grow in a very narrow space, a few tens of microns wide, between two parallel glass slides. In this space, the sponge grows in an almost bidimensional structure, where the relations between the mesohyl and the aquiferous system are particularly clear. The resulting preparations (*"sandwich cultures"*) combine some of the advantages of a histological preparation with those of an *in vivo* observation; they are specially suitable for time-lapse cinematography (Ankel, 1965, Efremova, 1967; Mawet and Rasmont, 1971; Rasmont and De Vos, 1974).

E. Feeding the Cultures

Sponges can be kept for weeks without being fed. During that period, they slowly digest their yolk reserves. It is probable too that they ingest the bacteria that develop in the medium on their own waste products. Counts have shown that there are from 10^2 to 10^3 live bacteria per milliliter in the medium of a 25-ml petri dish containing sponges from 120 gemmules. This is very low, considering the fact that we take no sterility precaution, except the initial cleansing of the gemmules. Many experiments can thus be made on sponge populations without feeding them, but in every case, preliminary comparisons should be made with nourished animals. Sponge cultures can be fed with suspensions of bacteria. We use *Escherichia coli*, thoroughly washed with sponge culture medium, killed by tyndallization and kept deep-frozen until use (Rasmont, 1961).

III. Factors of Gemmulation

A. Field Studies

In temperate climates, the gemmules are usually produced late in summer or at the beginning of autumn, in the oldest, deepest parts of the sponge. To this general rule, there are many exceptions. In *Spongilla lacustris*, deep and superficial parts of the sponge generate gemmules that are structurally and physiologically different (Jørgensen, 1946; Brøndsted and Brøndsted, 1953; Brøndsted and Løvtrup, 1953; Rasmont, 1954). In the same pond, sponges of different species gemmulate at different times (Simpson and Gilbert, 1973). From our experience, we know that individuals of *Ephydatia fluviatilis* of the same age, but of different strains, kept in the same pond, gemmulate at different times and that sponges of the same age and strain grow at a different pace and gemmulate at different times in different ponds. Finally, very small specimens of *E. fluviatilis* have been found to gemmulate in the field as early as mid-April (Rasmont, 1956).

From these field studies, one can only draw the conclusion that the triggering of gemmulation depends in a complex manner on intrinsic and environmental factors.

B. *In Vitro* STUDIES

The possibility of cultivating freshwater sponges under defined conditions made it feasible to analyze the factors of gemmulation *in vitro*.

1. Extrinsic Factors

The gemmulation rate of unfed sponges depends on temperature and on illumination. It is worth noticing, from an ecological point of view, that when these factors vary daily between two values, the rates of gemmulation are higher than when either factor is kept constant for a 24-hour period (Rasmont, 1970, 1974). Constant illumination, even at a very low level, inhibits gemmulation, whereas constant darkness does not. This is but one of the many effects of light on the metabolism of freshwater sponges; light also enhances the respiration of gemmules (Rasmont and Schmidt, 1967) and of sponges (Rasmont, 1970).

Since it involves the storage of yolk, gemmulation depends also on the quality and quantity of the food available to the sponge (Rasmont, 1963). A suitable diet of killed bacteria increases the production of gemmules.

2. Intrinsic Factors

a. *Genetic Differences.* The most prominent differences in the spontaneous rate of gemmulation of small sponges cultivated *in vitro* are species and even strain dependent. For *E. fluviatilis*, the four strains that we have studied from that point of view rank in the following order of decreasing ability to gemmulate: $\alpha > \delta > \beta > \gamma$.

b. Size. As described above, by incubating different numbers of gemmules in clusters, one obtains sponges of the same age, but of different
size, without this being due to feeding. Under these conditions, the rate
of gemmulation increases with the size of the sponge. Very small sponges
produce significantly smaller gemmules than wild sponges. This suggested
that it is not a given number of cells that is necessary to start a gemmule,
but rather a given proportion of the cell population in the sponge (Rasmont, 1963).

c. Cell Populations Equilibria. By incubating clusters of 3 gemmules
at day 0 and adding one gemmule at day 3, one obtains sponges that
hatched from 4 gemmules, but that differ from control 4 gemmule-sponges
in that the "late" gemmule germinates in an already developing sponge.
Sponges of the former type gemmulate sooner than the controls, and at
a pace that suggests that something contributed by the "late" gemmule
is either reused, or is somehow involved in the production of the new
gemmules (Rasmont, 1963).

It is conceivable that the onset of gemmulation may be dependent
on a concentration threshold of some blastogenic material, e.g., on the
population density of the archaeocytes or the trophocytes in the sponge.

d. The Action of Theophylline. Theophylline, in concentrations of
about 10^{-4} M, strongly stimulates gemmulation (Rasmont, 1974). Since
methylxanthines inhibit cAMP-phosphodiesterases (Robison *et al.*, 1971),
this effect of theophylline suggests that cAMP may play some role in
gemmulation. The fact that addition of cyclic nucleotides to the cultiva-
tion medium has no effect on the gemmulation rate does not exclude the
possible involvement of cAMP in gemmulation. It is conceivable that
extracellular gradients of cAMP concentration play a role in the aggregation of amoeboid cells in sponges, as they do in the aggregation of
amoebae in cellular slime molds (Konijn, 1972). A general rise in the
concentration of cAMP would not be expected to mimic the gradient,
whereas an inhibitor of cAMP-phosphodiesterase might facilitate its formation. Another possible explanation is that theophylline acts on the intracellular concentration of cAMP in a cell type which has a membrane
permeable to the methylxanthine, but not to the cyclic nucleotide.

e. The Population Density of Sponges. The gemmulation rate of
sponges in petri dishes is lower if the medium is periodically renewed,
and faster when it is left unchanged (Rasmont, 1963, 1974); this is the
case irrespective of feeding or stimulation with theophylline.

When sponges are cultivated in petri dishes so that the only variable
is the total number of sponges, and they are stimulated with theophylline,
the rate of gemmulation increases with increasing population density.
Since this is the case also for unfed sponges, it is unlikely that this effect

is a consequence of the depletion of food in high population densities. When an unfed population of sponges of strain β is stimulated with theophylline, its gemmulation rate is much lower than in a comparable population of strain α. In a mixed population of the same total size, the gemmulation rate of the α sponges is lower than in a pure α population, while the gemmulation of β is faster than in pure populations of that strain.

One possible explanation of these findings assumes the existence of a diffusible agent that participates in the triggering of gemmulation when its concentration in the sponge reaches an effective threshold. That agent would increase more rapidly in stagnant medium containing a large sponge population than under the opposite conditions. The action of this agent would not be strain specific, while the rate of its production would be. This hypothetical agent may be some trivial metabolite; this seems unlikely, however, considering the differences observed between different strains.

IV. Control of Hatching of Gemmules

A. DIAPAUSE VERSUS DIRECT INHIBITION

Neither the ecological function of the gemmules nor the mechanism by which they are kept from premature hatching is the same in all species. The differences can be illustrated by two local species.

In the case of *Ephydatia mulleri*, the sponge regresses in late summer to the extent that, by October, only the gemmules are left in the skeleton of the stem sponge. In this case, the gemmules constitute the sole reproductive reserve from which regeneration can take place in spring. In the autumn, the temperature is still higher than in spring, when the gemmules will hatch. They are kept from hatching prematurely by being in a state of diapause, as this state was defined by Agrell (1951). They must be vernalized, i.e., chilled, for several weeks before being able to hatch at a higher temperature (Rasmont, 1954). Recently, the gemmules of the marine species *Haliclona loosanoffi* have been reported to behave in the same way (Fell, 1974).

In *E. fluviatilis*, on the other hand, the regression of the sponge occurs only in late autumn. This regression affects principally the aquiferous system, whereas the mesohyl stays alive throughout the winter. The vernal regeneration of the sponge starts as a reorganization of this residual live tissue (Van de Vyver and Willenz, 1975) and the gemmules are not necessarily involved in the process. Therefore, rather than being a necessity for reproduction, the gemmules in this species are an insurance against incidental destruction of the sponge. These gemmules do not undergo diapause. They are able to hatch as soon as they are isolated from the parent sponge. On the other hand, as long as they lie within the parental mesohyl, they are prevented from hatching by an inhibitory substance secreted by the surrounding sponge itself (Rasmont, 1963).

B. GEMMULOSTASIN

This substance, provisionally referred to as *"gemmulostasin"* is diffusible in the medium. Its concentration can be measured and expressed in terms of biological activity units. Its activity is irreversibly suppressed by heating for 10 minutes at 100°C. It can be recovered from the medium and concentrated by evaporation under reduced pressure (Rasmont, 1965).

Work is in progress to purify and analyze it. It is dialyzable and, according to its properties in Sephadex chromatography, has a molecular weight of less than 1000. Its activity is not destroyed by Pronase. It appears to be efficient at very low concentrations, and it may be a synergistic association of two or more substances (S. Peiffer, A. Weisman, and R. Rasmont, unpublished data).

We know somewhat more about the biological effects of gemmulostasin than about its nature. It is not a general antimetabolite: it has no inhibitory effect on the growth of various bacteria, fungi, protozoa, nor on bryozoa statoblasts. In freshwater sponges, it is not strain or species specific; it is active on the gemmules of *E. fluviatilis*, and of *E. mulleri* after their diapause is over. However, a diapausing species like *E. mulleri* does not secrete it by itself, or at least not in amounts that could be detected in the medium, even after concentration.

Gemmulostasin interferes with the development of the gemmules only during the first 36 hours. Beyond that point, a rapidly increasing percentage of the gemmules become resistant to its action (Rozenfeld, 1970). As mentioned above, the only morphological change during the first 36 hours in untreated, developing gemmules is the separation of the nuclei. During the same period, the developing gemmules show a low level of incorporation of leucine-^{3}H into proteins and of uridine-^{3}H into RNA. Incorporation of thymidine-^{3}H, on the contrary, is characterized by a high peak, which probably corresponds to the S-phase preparatory for the first wave of karyokineses. The situation is strikingly different in gemmules that are inhibited by gemmulostasin: a high peak appears both in leucine-^{3}H and in uridine-^{3}H incorporation, while the normal peak in thymidine-^{3}H incorporation is completely prevented (Rozenfeld, 1974).

A curious and seemingly paradoxical finding is that when the shell of a gemmule is punctured with a fine needle at the beginning of incubation, the gemmule becomes insensitive to gemmulostasin. A few thesocytes, amounting to 2–5% of the total mass are expelled through the opening and burst. Those that remain in the hull develop in the presence of gemmulostasin quite normally, though somewhat more slowly than in its absence. Although the hatching occurs through the perforation, the digestion of the micropyle takes place as in normal development (Rozenfeld, 1971). Similarly, the diapause of dormant gemmules of *E. mulleri* is interrupted when their shell is punctured; their development goes on without previous vernalization (F. Rozenfeld, unpublished).

When gemmules of *E. fluviatilis* are incubated in large clusters, only those located at the periphery hatch, while the more central ones fail to develop (Kilian, 1964). Therefore, in our laboratory, when we want to raise a large sponge from a cluster of several hundreds of gemmules, we always arrange these in a line rather than in a massive cluster. Furthermore, the hatching of large numbers of gemmules in a small vessel is often very slow and incomplete, unless the medium is periodically renewed during incubation (R. Rasmont, unpublished).

These facts strongly suggest that the gemmules of sponges give off a substance that inhibits their own germination, in the way the spores of cellular slime molds do (Ceccarini, 1966). Although we do not know what this substance is, the simplest assumption is that it is similar to the gemmulostasin secreted by growing sponges.

C. A TENTATIVE EXPLANATION OF THE HIBERNATION MECHANISMS

Zeuthen (1939) has shown that during hibernation the gemmules of *Spongilla lacustris* undergo a large increase in osmotic pressure. As soon as they are completed, their osmotic pressure rises to values equivalent to 100–170 mM NaCl. This pressure decreases before hatching to values of about 25 mM NaCl, comparable to the intracellular pressure in nongemmulating sponges. The same phenomenon seems to occur also in *E. fluviatilis* (Schmidt, 1970).

By fractionating gemmule extracts, Zeuthen came to the conclusion that the substance responsible for the increase in osmotic pressure has a molecular weight of 146, provided it is not dissociated; its chemical identity, however, remained unknown.

A transitory increase in osmotic pressure is common among dormant stages of various organisms. When diapause starts in the egg of the silkworm *Bombyx mori*, a large proportion of the glycogen store is reversibly converted into sorbitol and glycerol (Chino, 1958). Clegg and Filosa (1961) showed that 7% of the dry weight of mature spores of cellular slime molds consists of trehalose. In the dormant ascospores of *Neuro-*

spora, Sussman (1961) found that trehalose formed a large part of the reserves. In both cases, activation of the spores is correlated with the synthesis of threhalase and the resulting hydrolysis of the carbohydrate.

It is interesting that, during the elaboration of a gemmule, the last morphological event is the disappearance of glycogen from the yolk platelets (De Vos, 1971); this occurs only after completion of the shell which is impermeable to carbohydrates (Simpson *et al.*, 1973). Thus, the increase in the osmotic pressure in the gemmule may be due to the accumulation of a carbohydrate, which is derived from the degradation of glycogen and is not further catabolized because of absence or inactivity of the suitable enzyme.

Simpson *et al.* (1973) suggested that the gemmulostasin effect might be due to the accumulation in the medium "of mixed solutes (excretory and breakdown products, ions) with an osmotic pressure high enough to inhibit hatching." Our information about gemmulostasin does not substantiate this suggestion. Simpson *et al.* stress the rather high ratio of organic contents to water (8 gemmules per milliliter) in our gemmulo-stasin-producing cultures. However, comparable cultures of *E. mulleri* do not secrete any detectable gemmulostasin, despite the fact that the gemmules of this species are about twice the volume of those of *E. fluviatilis* (Rosenfeld, 1970). Furthermore, cultures of *E. fluviatilis* produce under constant illumination about half as much gemmulostasin as comparable cultures in constant darkness (F. Rozenfeld, unpublished) although their respiratory metabolism is higher under the former condition (Rasmont, 1970). Finally, one does not see how the gemmulostasin effect would be irreversibly suppressed by heating (Rasmont, 1965) if it were due simply to a rise in osmotic pressure.

On the other hand, we know that in the presence of gemmulostasin, the intragemmular osmotic pressure is maintained at a high level; and that, even in the absence of gemmulostasin, the development of gemmules can be reversibly inhibited by keeping them in saline solutions of suitable concentration (Simpson *et al.*, 1973; I. Schmidt, unpublished). This indicates that variations in the osmotic pressure of the gemmules play a major role in the control of their development, as Simpson *et al.* suggested.

Furthermore, the presence of gemmulostasin results in a block to pre-prophasic synthesis of DNA and, consequently, in the inhibition of cell division and development. There are indications, however, that these effects are mediated rather than direct.

1. Gemmulostasin has no effect on cell multiplication in organisms other than sponge gemmules. This makes it unlikely that it plays a direct role in the fundamental process of DNA replication.

2. On gemmules, it is active only during a very early phase of their development, although mitoses proceed until after hatching.

3. Although the shell of the gemmule must be permeable to gemmulostasin, puncturing the shell has the paradoxical result of rendering the gemmule insensitive to its action.

Finally, the fact that gemmulostasin brings about an early peak in uridine and leucine incorporation could be regarded as an indication that it derepresses some genes coding for the synthesis of proteins.

Putting together all these indications, we come to the following hypotheses, regarding the action of gemmulostasin:

1. Gemmulostasin causes an intragemmular inhibitor to appear. The proteins corresponding to the peak in leucine incorporation could be either this inhibitor itself or some enzymes involved in its synthesis.

2. This inhibitor blocks a step in the catabolism of glycogen, thus causing the accumulation of a catabolite of low molecular weight.

3. This results in an increase in osmotic pressure, which, in turn, acts on the synthesis of DNA.

The effect of puncturing the shell fits with this hypothetical scheme in at least two ways. The puncture may allow the outflow of the catabolite itself, thereby diminishing the osmotic pressure directly; or it may allow the intragemmular inhibitor to escape from the gemmule, thereby suppressing the block responsible for the accumulation of the catabolite.

Anyhow, since the gemmules become insensitive to the action of gemmulostasin after the second day of incubation, there must exist some feedback loop between a late step in the development, e.g., the drop in osmotic pressure, and one of the earlier events, e.g., the synthesis of the putative intragemmular inhibitor.

All the physiological similarities and differences between the gemmules of *E. mulleri* and those of *E. fluviatilis* could be accounted for by assuming that, in the former species, the production of gemmulostasin is restricted to the gemmules themselves, and that it is produced or stored there in larger concentrations than in the gemmules of *E. fluviatilis*. Furthermore, if an event that arrests development, (e.g., synthesis of gemmulostasin) is slowed down by low temperature more than an event conducive to development (e.g., outward diffusion of gemmulostasin), then exposure to cold (vernalization) should facilitate the development of the gemmule. This would account for the diapause of gemmules of *E. mulleri*.

Therefore, a single hypothesis might account for all that we know about the control of development of diapausing and of nondiapausing gemmules; according to this hypothesis, the action of gemmulostasin is mediated by an intragemmular, nondiffusible inhibitor which, in turn, is responsible for the other phenomena of developmental arrest.

V. Control of Cell Differentiation

Two aspects of differentiation in freshwater sponges have been examined in our laboratory: the secretion of the skeletal spicules, and the morphogenesis of the aquiferous system.

A. DIFFERENTIATION OF THE SILICEOUS SKELETON

It is presently impossible to distinguish a scleroblast from an archaeocyte by morphological criteria, except by the presence of the growing spicule itself. There are some indications that archaeocytes can produce spicules in the absence of any other differentiation. F. Rozenfeld (unpublished) has found that gemmules can hatch in puromycin (7 $\mu g/ml$); in this condition, they give rise exclusively to archaeocytes that are scattered on the substratum, do not move, and do not digest their yolk. However, many of these archaeocytes produce a spicule, before eventually disintegrating. This suggests that among all other differentiation events in the sponge, the making of a spicule requires least new protein synthesis.

Although a scleroblast cannot be identified as a distinct cell type, before or after it has formed a spicule, the elaboration of each spicule can be regarded as an individual event in the array of differentiation steps involved in the making of a sponge. This phenomenon is particularly worth studying because the formation of spicules results in an obvious and indestructible product, and the problem can therefore be tackled on a quantitative basis.

During the first days of their development, small individuals of *E. fluviatilis* expel some of their newly formed spicules through the osculum (Rasmont, 1963; Mawet and Rasmont, 1971). In unfed sponges, this elimination sets in as soon as the aquiferous system is complete, increases during the following week, and then slows down. Comparing sponges grown from 2, 4, or 6 gemmules, these authors found the total production of spicules to be approximately proportional to the size of the sponges, whereas the number of spicules expelled varied in proportion to the square of that size. Pé (1973) studied the total spicule production of 1-gemmule sponges, either nourished or not. In unfed specimens, the production of spicules came to a halt as soon as the sponge attained the maximum size it can reach on its own reserves, i.e., within 4 days after hatching. On the other hand, in fed sponges, both growth and formation of spicules are continued for the duration of the 3 weeks' experiment. Pé also confirmed the observation (Rasmont, 1963) that, when fed, sponges expel few, if any, spicules.

These observations show that in a normally developing sponge, spicule production is in some way controlled by the needs of the sponge, i.e., by the size of the skeleton that is needed for its scaffolding. On the other hand, the experiments of Mawet and Rasmont suggest that this feedback is established only after morphogenesis has reached an advanced stage, and that, at earlier stages, spicules are made by a certain proportion of the hatching cells, irrespective of the "needs" of the developing sponge.

As would be expected, the production of spicules is controlled not only by internal factors, but also by the silicate contents of the water. Various studies (Jewell, 1935; Jørgensen, 1944, 1947) have shown that the size of spicules and, in the case of *Spongilla lacustris*, the number of microscleres produced decrease when the silica contents of the water is lowered. However, Pé (1973) compared sponges growing in media containing 1.5, 15, and 60 mg of silica per liter and found that although the spicules are more slender when the concentration of silica is lowest, they form in greater number under these conditions and in smaller number when the silica is more concentrated. Therefore, within these limits, the silica content of the water seems to exert a negative feedback on the number of spicules produced. How this feedback works is unknown.

B. DIFFERENTIATION OF THE AQUIFEROUS SYSTEM

The inhibition of DNA synthesis by hydroxyurea interferes with the development of sponges from gemmules (F. Rozenfeld, unpublished). At concentrations about 4 mM, hydroxyurea irreversibly inhibits hatching; in 1 mM hydroxyurea, more than 90% of the gemmules hatch, but develop very aberrantly. The cells form a hollow dome of pinacoderm, with the roof stretched on spicules like a tent on its poles. Most strikingly, the aquiferous system is completely absent. Instead, the floor of the pinacodermal cavity is covered with a layer of uninucleated archaeocytes, rich with undigested yolk (Figs. 1–4). Kept in hydroxyurea, this structure can survive for several days in the same condition. However, this condition can be reversed toward normal development by removal of the hydroxyurea; if the preparations are transferred to normal medium, an outburst of mitoses takes place and numerous choanocyte chambers are produced. These line up along newly formed pinacodermal vesicles, giving rise to disorderly, discontinuous, and often blind segments of ducts. Only later on do these segments arrange themselves gradually into a coherent aquiferous system.

The reversible inhibition of the formation of the aquiferous system by hydroxyurea is readily explainable on the basis of what is known about normal morphogenesis of this system. Brien (1932) and later Wintermann (1951) showed that the choanocytes arise through successive divisions of archaeocytes, and that each choanocyte chamber originates by

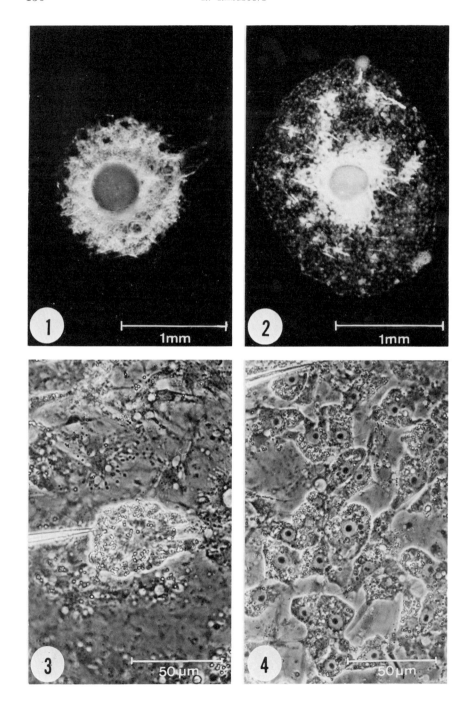

repeated divisions of a single archaeocyte. By inhibiting the proliferation of archaeocytes, hydroxyurea prevents preferentially the formation of cell lines which lead to the differentiation of choanocytes. Thus, the reaction of gemmules to hydroxyurea offers a new possibility for studying differentiation in these systems.

VI. General Remarks

As pointed out in a recent review (Pavans de Ceccatty, 1974), developmental and functional coordination of the sponge involves (a) nonpermanent cell contacts; (b) more permanent contacts, either between cells, or of cells with intercellular connective elements; (c) diffusible chemical signals.

Comparing freshwater sponges with higher metazoans, we find that sponges have fewer distinct cell-types; that their differentiation is more readily reversible, under relatively simple experimental or natural conditions; and that most of the cells within the sponge are highly mobile, especially the less specialized cell types.

It is therefore conceivable that the chemical signals which coordinate cell differentiation in sponges are less numerous than in higher metazoa and that they function throughout the life of the sponge, rather than being restricted to an initial period of morphogenesis.

Because of these features, sponges offer certain special possibilities and advantages for studying fundamental mechanisms of differentiation and morphogenesis.

VII. Summary

The asexual reproduction of freshwater sponges has been studied on small individuals cultivated in petri dishes.

1. The formation of gemmules depends on ecological factors (temperature, illumination, nutrition, population density) and on intrinsic factors (strain, size, cell population equilibria). Gemmulation is enhanced by theophylline.

FIG. 1. *Ephydatia fluviatilis*, 8 days' incubation in mineral medium. The central dark body is the empty shell of the stem gemmule, surrounded by the well-developed aquiferous system.

FIG. 2. *Ephydatia fluviatilis*, 8 days, in 1.3 mM hydroxyurea. The aquiferous system is lacking; the empty shell is surrounded by a dense population of archaeocytes.

FIG. 3. A choanocyte chamber on a background of pinacocytes in a normally developing sponge.

FIG. 4. Dense population of uninucleated archaeocytes in a hydroxyurea-treated sponge.

An explanatory scheme is proposed, involving (a) supraliminar accumulation of a blastogenic material, (b) sponge-to-sponge communication through a diffusible agent, and (c) cell chemotaxis conducive to the pre-gemmular aggregate. One of these steps may be cAMP dependent.

2. The development of gemmules is arrested either by a diffusible substance (gemmulostasin) secreted by the stem sponge, or by diapause. This arrest is suppressed by puncturing the shell of the gemmule. Gemmulostasin blocks preprophasic DNA synthesis.

It is proposed that both forms of developmental arrest depend on the intragemmular synthesis of an inhibitor, which blocks a particular step in the degradation of glycogen, thus causing a rise in osmotic pressure.

3. The differentiation of two cell lines has been followed during the development of a sponge from the gemmule.

The production and utilization of spicules is regulated by the nutritional state of the sponge and by the silica content of the water. It is suggested that silica concentration exerts a negative feedback on the number of spicules.

The differentiation of collar cells is blocked by concentrations of hydroxyurea that allow hatching of the gemmule. It is suggested that this is due to selective blocking of the cell line that requires the highest number of mitoses.

REFERENCES

Agrell, I. (1951). *Annee Biol.* **27**, 287–295.
Ankel, W. E. (1965). *Zool. Anz., Suppl.* **28**, 426–444.
Ankel, W. E., and Eigenbrodt, H. (1950). *Zool. Anz.* **145**, 195–204.
Berthold, G. (1969). *Z. Wiss. Mikrosk.* **69**, 227–243.
Bonner, J. T., ed. (1967). "The Cellular Slime Molds." Princeton Univ. Press, Princeton, New Jersey.
Borojevic, R., Fry, W. G., Jones, W. C., Levi, C., Rasmont, R., Sara, M., and Vacelet, J. (1968). *Bull. Mus. Hist. Natur., Paris* **39**, 1224–1235.
Brien, P. (1932). *Arch. Zool. Exp. Gen.* **74**, 461–506.
Brøndsted, A., and Brøndsted, H. V. (1953). *Vidensk. Medd. Dansk Naturh. Foren.* **115**, 133–144.
Brøndsted, H. V., and Løvtrup, E. (1953). *Vidensk. Medd. Dansk Naturh. Foren.* **115**, 145–157.
Ceccarini, C. (1966). Ph.D. Thesis (cited in "The Cellular Slime Molds" Bonner, 1967, p. 80).
Chino, H. (1958). *J. Insect Physiol.* **2**, 1–12.
Clegg, J. S., and Filosa, M. F. (1961). *Nature (London)* **192**, 1077–1078.
De Vos, L. (1971). *J. Microsc. (Paris)* **10**, 283–304.
De Vos, L. (1972). *J. Microsc. (Paris)* **15**, 247–252.
De Vos, L., and Rozenfeld, F. (1974). *J. Microsc. (Paris)* **20**, 333–338.
Efremova, S. M. (1967). *Acta Biol. (Budapest)* **18**, 37–46.
Fell, P. E. (1974). *Biol. Bull.* **147**, 333–351.
Hyman, L. H. (1940). "The Invertebrates," Vol. I. McGraw-Hill, New York.

Jewell, M. E. (1935). *Ecol. Monogr.* 5, 461–504.

Jørgensen, C. B. (1944). *Kgl. Dan. Vidensk. Selsk., Biol. Medd.* 19, 1–45.

Jørgensen, C. B. (1946). *Vidensk. Medd. Dansk Naturh. Foren.* 109, 69–79.

Jørgensen, C. B. (1947). *Kgl. Dan. Vidensk. Selsk., Biol Medd.* 20, 1–21.

Kilian, E. F. (1964). *Zool. Beitr.* 10, 85–159.

Konijn, T. M. (1972). *Advan. Cyclic Nucleotide Res.* 1, 17–31.

Leveaux, M. (1939). *Ann. Soc. Roy. Zool. Belg.* 70, 53–96.

Mawet, A., and Rasmont, R. (1971). *Arch. Biol.* 82, 543–565.

Pavans de Ceccatty, M. (1974). *Amer. Zool.* 14, 895–903.

Pé, J. (1973). *Arch. Biol.* 84, 147–173.

Rasmont, R. (1954). *Bull. Cl. Sci., Acad. Roy. Belg.* 40, 288–304.

Rasmont, R. (1956). *Ann. Soc. Roy. Zool. Belg.* 86, 349–387.

Rasmont, R. (1961). *Ann. Soc. Roy. Zool. Belg.* 91, 147–156.

Rasmont, R. (1963). *Develop. Biol.* 8, 243–271.

Rasmont, R. (1965). *C. R. Acad. Sci.* 261, 845–846.

Rasmont, R. (1970). *Symp. Zool. Soc. London* 25, 415–422.

Rasmont, R. (1974). *Experientia* 30, 792–794.

Rasmont, R., and De Vos, L. (1974). *Arch. Biol.* 85, 329–341.

Rasmont, R., and Schmidt, I. (1967). *Comp. Biochem. Physiol.* 23, 959–967.

Robison, G. A., Butcher, R. W., and Sutherland, E. W. (1971). "Cyclic AMP." Academic Press, New York.

Rozenfeld, F. (1970). *Arch. Biol.* 81, 193–214.

Rozenfeld, F. (1971). *Arch. Biol.* 82, 103–113.

Rozenfeld, F. (1974). *J. Embryol. Exp. Morphol.* 32, 287–295.

Ruthman, A. (1965). *Quart. J. Microsc. Sci.* 106, 99–114.

Schmidt, I. (1970). *C. R. Acad. Sci.* 271, 924–927.

Simons, J. R., and Müller, L. (1966). *Nature (London)* 210, 847–848.

Simpson, T. L., and Gilbert, J. J. (1973). *Trans. Amer. Microsc. Soc.* 92, 422–433.

Simpson, T. L., Vaccaro, C. A., and Shàafi, R. I. (1973). *Z. Morphol. Tiere* 76, 339–357.

Strekal, T. A., and McDiffett, W. F. (1974). *Biol. Bull.* 146, 267–278.

Sussman, A. S. (1961). *Quart. Rev. Biol.* 36, 109–116.

Van de Vyver, G. (1970). *Ann. Embryol. Morphol.* 3, 251–262.

Van de Vyver, G., and Willenz, P. (1975). *Wilhelm Roux' Arch. Entwicklungsmech. Organismen.* 177, 41–52.

Wintermann, G. (1951). *Zool. Jahrb., Abt. Anat. Ontog. Tiere* 71, 427–486.

Zeuthen, E. (1939). *Z. Vergl. Physiol.* 26, 537–547.

CHAPTER 6

DIFFERENTIATION OF THE GOLGI APPARATUS IN THE GENETIC CONTROL OF DEVELOPMENT

W. G. Whaley, Marianne Dauwalder, and T. P. Leffingwell

THE CELL RESEARCH INSTITUTE
THE UNIVERSITY OF TEXAS AT AUSTIN
AUSTIN, TEXAS

I. Introduction

There is increasing evidence that cellular membranes and their changing constituents represent one of the principal mechanisms by which the genome and its modifiers operate in determining the specific characteristics of cells of different types and different species (see D. Bennett *et al.*, 1972; Boyse, 1973; Moscona, 1974a). There is now general agreement that the Golgi apparatus is responsible for the production of a wide range of secretory products characteristic of different types of cells and that it also makes a contribution to the surface membrane (see Northcote, 1971a,b, 1973; Rambourg, 1971; Whaley *et al.*, 1972; Cook, 1973). The contribution may be selective and only transient, and the rate of renewal or turnover in various regions of the cell membrane may differ greatly. The total material transported from this intracellular organelle to the surface includes lipids, proteins, and carbohydrates in various patterns of association. These compounds lend selective characteristics and specific properties as well as general properties to the cell surface (for references, see Winzler, 1970; Cook, 1970; Kraemer, 1971; Cook and Stoddart, 1973; Oseroff *et al.*, 1973; Ito, 1974; Bretscher, 1974), and when returned to the cytoplasm may also affect significantly the metabolism within the cell (see Dingle, 1969; Dauwalder *et al.*, 1972).

The proposition that the plasma membrane of the cell is largely assembled internally and then transported to its surface position, together with considerable indirect but convincing supporting evidence, has been summarized by Whaley *et al.* (1972), Dauwalder *et al.* (1972), Cook (1973),

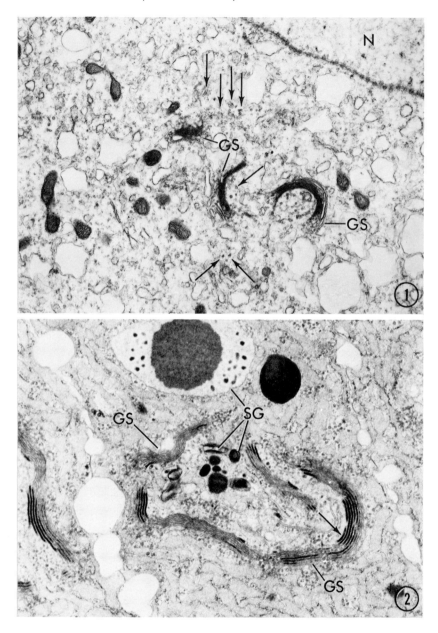

Fig. 1. Golgi apparatus in a young oocyte of the snail *Helix aspersa*. The stacks (GS) are relatively simple and dispersed in small groups in the cytoplasm. At this stage there is no obvious production of secretory or storage products, but small vesicles (arrows), whose origin and function have not been defined, can be seen near the Golgi stacks. The polarity of the organelle is not highly developed. The

and Whaley (1975). Since there is considerable evidence that the composition and patterning of surface groups reflect both the influence of the genome and the participation of the Golgi apparatus, the implication is that the Golgi apparatus represents one stage in the elucidation of the characteristics controlled by the genome and its modifiers. It should be noted, however, that the surface membrane is a dynamic structure subject to further modification in relation to its environment and particular functions. The Golgi apparatus thus appears to be a terminal or near terminal stage in the control of assembly of macromolecular "information." It therefore becomes of concern to consider how this control may take place, notably because there is accumulating evidence that much of the regulation of development and its modification takes place in part in response to activities of surface membranes (see Moscona, 1974a). This paper will be concerned mainly with certain questions related to the Golgi apparatus and the dynamics of the plasma membrane. In this function the activity of the Golgi apparatus is linked more or less conspicuously to secretion. For a review of its functioning in secretion and a much more extensive treatment of the literature, see Whaley (1975).

The Golgi apparatus is characteristically composed of smooth membranes, and the likelihood of its "control" of the advanced stages of the assembly of molecular information by mechanisms involving nucleic acids seems remote. On the other hand, the likelihood of control of certain reactions by enzymatic proteins which are a part of, or intimately associated with, the membranes seems a reasonable possibility. Such proteins may act in the classic sense as "agents" of the genes. There may, of course, be significant interactions between the proteins and other components of the membranes.

The Golgi apparatus differs from other organelles in that in the usual form there is generally a detectable polarity of maturation from one face of the apparatus to the other. This polarity may not be readily visible in very early stages of development, but it clearly accompanies differenti-

---

apparatus does become highly active in later stages of oogenesis. The structural features seen here are very similar to those seen in the cleaving eggs. Glutaraldehyde/osmium. N = nucleus. ×10,000.

FIG. 2. A portion of the very large, localized, and quite complex Golgi apparatus from the multifid gland of *Helix aspersa* during the reproductive season. The organelle is highly polarized with accumulations of electron dense secretory materials in the more distal cisternae (arrows) of the Golgi stacks (GS). The apparatus occurs in the cell between the nucleus and the secretory lumen, and in longitudinal sections the region occupied by the organelle may be more than 25 μm in length and 15 μm in width. The cisternae appear to be very elongate or highly interconnected or both. Glutaraldehyde/osmium. SG = secretory granules in various stages of maturation. ×11,500.

ation, which also involves form changes in the organelle (Figs. 1 and 2 show different forms in the same organism). This polarity involves both the characteristics of membranes of the cisternae and their activities. It raises questions concerning the origin of the apparatus and the manner of its functioning, and it raises problems in the use of terms in describing it. Many of the former are still unresolved; for an extended discussion of the latter, see Dauwalder *et al.* (1972). The authors have here adopted the term "distal" to indicate the face that is usually seen to be more active in the evolution of membrane-bounded secretory products, and the term "proximal" to indicate the opposite face, which appears to be where the membranes are formed. The membranes of the cisternae on the distal face as well as their contents can sometimes be seen to be distinctly different from those at the proximal face. Whether or not this implies a progressive displacement of cisternae across the stack, as postulated on the basis of radioautographic experiments by Neutra and Leblond (1966a) and by some other investigators (see Mollenhauer and Morré, 1966; Brown, 1969), is not clear. Such displacement may occur in some instances, but not in others, or rates of displacement, if it occurs, may differ considerably. In fact, under certain conditions or in some stages of development, the general form of the organelle may be quite different (see Whaley, 1975), and the possibility for such a displacement would seem unlikely. The current evidence is that, in the stacked form of the Golgi apparatus, membranes are somehow assembled at one face and greatly modified in functional capabilities toward the other face.

A common assumption has been that membrane-bounded vesicles are transferred from the endoplasmic reticulum and/or the nuclear envelope to the proximal face of the apparatus to fuse and form new cisternae periodically (for example Morré *et al.*, 1971; Kessel, 1971). This postulate has been challenged on the basis of differences in membrane composition by Meldolesi *et al.* (1971a–c) (for additional information and references, see Meldolesi, 1974), and by numerous investigators on the basis of the fact that transferred products usually appear first toward the distal face (for references, see Whaley, 1975). While the differentiation of the apparatus is of concern here, questions about the origin of the membranes of the cisternae cannot be answered beyond noting that their formation may be a continuing process, as is their extension, and that the Golgi apparatus represents a region in which they become greatly modified as well as substantially extended (see Whaley, 1966). The assembly of cisternal membranes can be substantially increased by some experimental procedures (Hall and Witkus, 1964; Whaley *et al.*, 1964) that differ appreciably from those that modify the formation of secretory products (e.g., Weinstock, 1970; Seegmiller *et al.*, 1971, 1972b).

II. Morphological Differentiation

Yamamoto observed as early as 1963 (Yamamoto, 1963) that there were sometimes differences between the thickness of membranes of Golgi apparatus-derived vesicles and such membranes as those of the nuclear envelope and the Golgi cisternae, the former approaching in thickness the plasma membrane. Helminen and Ericsson (1968) noted changes in the membrane surrounding milk proteins in mammary gland cells, which they ascribed to a thickening of the membranes as the milk proteins passed through the Golgi apparatus preparatory to secretion. Grove et al. (1968) pictured distinct changes in membrane thickness within the Golgi stack of cells of a fungus, indicating that the more proximal membranes resembled the nuclear envelope and the endoplasmic reticulum in thickness, and the more distal ones had increased to resemble the thickness of the plasma membrane. Hicks (1966) had shown that in the transitional epithelium of the rat bladder, changes in membrane thickness could be seen in localized cisternal regions ("patches") within the Golgi stack and suggested that these represented the sites of assembly of the specialized thick cell membrane of this tissue. The unique morphology and unusual composition of the plasma membrane of the mammalian bladder has been further discussed by Hicks et al. (1974), and although, as will be noted later, there may be additional changes in the membrane during transit from the apparatus to the cell surface, these data imply a highly specialized capacity for membrane organization at sites within the apparatus. Ovtracht and Thiéry (1972) have also suggested on the basis of cytochemical evidence that segments of the Golgi cisternae may be functionally differentiated. Thus, there is evidence that at or toward the distal face, the Golgi apparatus has the capacity to form differentiated membrane similar in morphology to the plasma membrane, and that this function may even be expressed in discrete regions of the individual cisternae.

The polarity can also frequently be demonstrated by the accumulation of secretory products only in cisternae close to one face of the organelle (Fig. 2), or, in some cases, only in vesicles associated with one face of the organelle (Fig. 3). In fact, the now classic pattern of the functioning of the apparatus in the production of zymogen in the pancreatic exocrine gland, supported not only by micrographs but by tracing the migration of constituent amino acids (for references, see Leblond, 1965; Palade, 1966), shows a preferential transfer to the so-called condensing vacuoles associated with the distal face of the apparatus. Although Palade's group has shown some concentration of zymogen in the Golgi stack (Jamieson and Palade, 1971), again this concentration is limited to the distal face. Indeed, the pattern of product accumulation only within the more distal

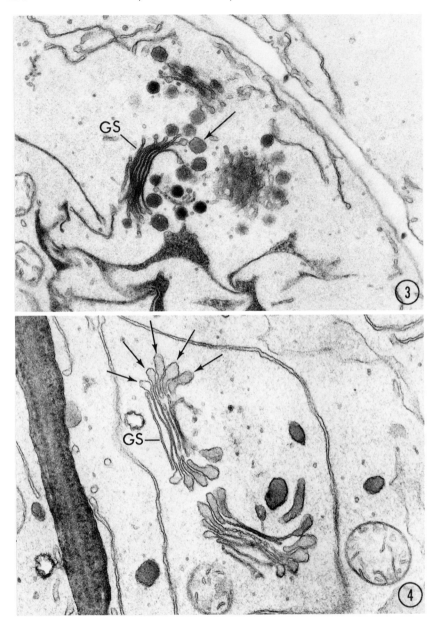

FIG. 3. Golgi stacks (GS) in a secreting epidermal cell of the root tip of *Zea mays*. The stacks occur dispersed in the cytoplasm but are highly active in the production of predominantly polysaccharide secretory materials in spherical vesicles (arrow) formed at the distal face. The vesicle contents are released by exocytosis

cisternae (suggesting perhaps the selective migration of substrate into these cisternae) exists in so many instances that it strongly supports the concept of maturational modification in the membranes, making possible the development of secretory products only after some specific changes have taken place. It should be noted, however, that other patterns also occur. Whether they reflect different developmental states of the organelle, different life-spans of cells, or the influence of other factors is not clear. For example, in certain cells of the rootcap which represent a terminal stage of development (the cells do not divide, and will be sloughed from the cap and die), the whole stack, or nearly all of it, appears to be hypertrophied, with an accumulation of secretory products (Fig. 4).

In some dysfunctions, genetically or experimentally induced, there is a distinct modification of the organization and hypertrophy of the Golgi apparatus (for example, Seegmiller et al., 1971, 1972a,b; Platzer and Gluecksohn-Waelsch, 1972; Landis, 1973). There are not only modifications in the morphology of the membranes across the stack, but also compositional modifications that may reflect changes in the permeability of the membrane or in the activity of membrane-associated enzymes so that the distal cisternae are functionally different from those at the proximal face—in other words, there is physiological differentiation within the organelle. The differentiation can be modified or even prevented experimentally. When it is, the secretory function may be modified, but in some instances the formation of cisternal envelopes may continue (Fig. 5). The introduction of certain viruses may also greatly modify the organization of the apparatus, for the virus particles seem to accumulate within vesicles or vacuoles possibly derived from the organelle (see Dales, 1971) (Fig. 6). In some instances, the virus-containing vacuoles may be related to the lysosomal system of the cell (see Della Torre, 1974), which might also reflect a functional interaction with the Golgi apparatus. In either case the presence of viruses may cause a substantial disruption of the Golgi region. There is also the question of whether some virus particles may acquire their envelope directly from the Golgi apparatus rather than

---

primarily toward the outer surface of the root, where they contribute to the thickened protective wall surrounding the root proper. KMnO₄. ×21,500.

Fig. 4. Golgi stacks (GS) in an outer cap cell of the root tip of Zea mays. The accumulation of secretory product (arrows) is associated with many of the cisternae and is not limited to those at the distal face. The form of the vesicles and the density of their content differ from those in the epidermal cells. The secretory product is polysaccharide in nature and contributes to the "slime" surrounding the rootcap. The stacks are dispersed in the cytoplasm, and in a typical longitudinal section more than 60 stacks can commonly be seen per cell KMnO₄. ×24,000. From Dauwalder et al. (1969).

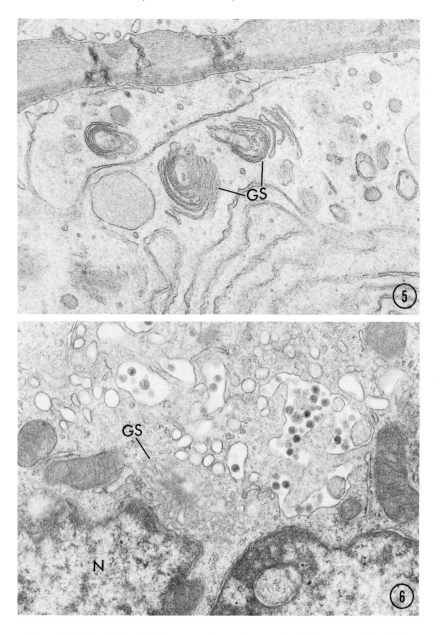

Fig. 5. Golgi stacks (GS) in an outer rootcap cell of *Zea mays* after 6 hours of treatment with a nitrogen atmosphere. As compared with Fig. 4, it can be seen that the form of the stacks is modified, the evolution of secretion vesicles is inhibited, but the formation of cisternae has apparently continued, as indicated by the increased number of cisternae per stack. KMnO₄. ×25,000.

from the plasma membrane (for which there is considerable evidence). If our hypothesis that much of the plasma membrane may be derived from the Golgi apparatus is correct, this may not be as great a difference as it might seem.

III. Enzymatic Differentiation

Physiological differentiation can also be demonstrated for a number of different classes of compounds by using cytochemical techniques. Among these, the techniques for enzyme localization have provided considerable information. Early in the study of the organelle by electron microscopy, Novikoff and his group (see Holtzman et al., 1967) began investigation of nucleoside phosphatases in the Golgi apparatus because workable techniques were available and on the chance that the transfer of membrane might be demonstrated. The technique was not successful in demonstrating the transfer of membrane, but it did indicate the presence of certain phosphatases. The general functioning of most of these phosphatases is still not known, but some of them have assumed an importance both in studying differentiation of the organelle and in the interpretation of some of its functions. Figure 7 shows an indication of inosine diphosphatase confined to the distal face of the Golgi apparatus. Dauwalder et al. (1969) have noted that in maize root tips the appearance of the inosine diphosphatase parallels some hypertrophy of these cisternae and the onset of a mucoid secretion. This reaction, by the way, has been observed in vertebrates (Fig. 7), invertebrates (Fig. 8), phanerogams (Fig. 9), and cryptogams (Fig. 10).

Thiamine pyrophosphatase (Fig. 11) has proved to be a general, though not universal, marker for the organelle, and Kessel (1971) has used it as a marker for vesicles derived from the nuclear envelope that he believes may develop into Golgi apparatus in grasshopper eggs.

The Golgi apparatus is also known to play a key role in the production of lysosomal enzymes. These enzymes are critical cellular constituents in intracellular digestion and in the modeling and remodeling of the surface constituents of the cell (Dingle, 1969). Among this group of enzymes, acid phosphatase has long been accepted as a marker. Acid phosphatase can frequently be identified in the more distal cisternae, or it sometimes occurs in what appear to be smooth endoplasmic reticulum

FIG. 6. A portion of the Golgi region of a Friend murine leukemia cell. A large aggregation of vacuoles containing viruslike particles is typically seen in close proximity to the Golgi apparatus. The Golgi stock (GS) included is sectioned tangentially; other stacks (not pictured) occur toward the periphery of the aggregation of vacuoles. Material provided by Dr. Boyd A. Hardesty. Glutaraldehyde/osmium. N = nucleus. ×27,000.

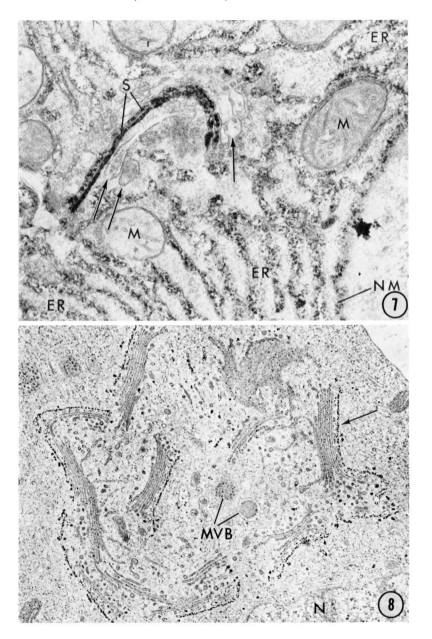

FIG. 7. A Golgi stack in a rat liver cell reacted to show the presence of inosine diphosphatase. The reaction product is seen in the two cisternae (saccules, S) toward the distal face. In liver cells some reaction product also occurs in the endoplasmic

segments close to the distal face (see Holtzman *et al.*, 1967; P. M. Novikoff *et al.*, 1971) (Fig. 12). Of importance to the interpretation of the functioning of the Golgi apparatus is that very often the various phosphatases and other enzymes that have been localized within the apparatus can be found to be limited to one or a few discrete cisternae within the stack—i.e., consistent with a high degree of specialization within the apparatus itself.

A more direct functional interpretation has been suggested for the localization of acyltransferases by members of Barrnett's group (Levine *et al.*, 1972; Benes *et al.*, 1973). They have found the cytochemical product localized within regions of the Golgi apparatus, in vesicles apparently derived from the apparatus, and in some tissues at the plasma membrane, and they proposed that this may reflect phospholipid synthesis for growth of the Golgi membranes and/or formation of membranes at this site to be moved into the plasma membrane. They did not find evidence for a movement of these enzymes from the rough endoplasmic reticulum to the Golgi apparatus, and they suggested from additional data that "the appearance of their activity in the Golgi complex may be a function of control factors which stimulate or repress plasma membrane biogenesis." These findings strongly support the concept that the Golgi apparatus is a center for the organization, extension, and specialization of the plasma membrane (see Whaley, 1966; Sjöstrand, 1968; Whaley *et al.*, 1971). All these and the subsequent data indicate that the surface membrane is preformed rather than formed epigenetically, as long supposed. In this preformation process it seems obviously to be given certain key characteristics by the Golgi apparatus.

Also of functional importance is the finding that certain glycosyltransferases occur in association with the Golgi apparatus. Unfortunately, evidence concerning them is not directly comparable to the cytochemically demonstrated enzymes because methods for their *in situ* location are not yet available, but a number of investigators have demonstrated the presence of certain glycosyltransferases in so-called "Golgi-rich frac-

---

reticulum (ER) and nuclear envelope (NM). The arrows indicate Golgi vacuoles without reaction product. M = mitochondria. ×36,000. From Novikoff (1965).

FIG. 8. The Golgi apparatus of the spermatocyte of *Helix aspersa* showing localization of inosine diphosphatase. The reaction product is localized in one or two cisternae (arrow) at what appears morphologically to be the proximal face. The activities of the Golgi apparatus at this stage in spermatogenesis have not yet been well defined although an unusual number of multivesicular bodies (MVB) are seen in the Golgi region. Additional information is needed for a more definitive interpretation. N = nucleus. ×17,000.

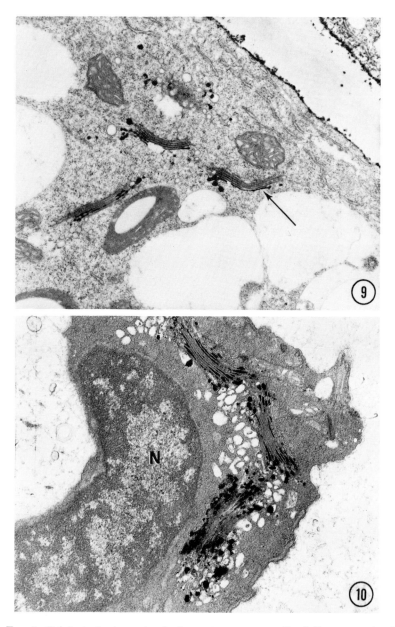

Fig. 9. Golgi stacks in a developing outer rootcap cell of *Zea mays* showing localization of inosine diphosphatase. The product is not strictly limited, but is often fairly discretely localized in cisternae toward the distal face (arrow). In this cell lineage the less differentiated cells (the cap initials) showed no reaction product

tions." Although clear standards for assessing the purity of such fractions have not yet been established, fractions of smooth microsomal membranes, which by current morphological and biochemical criteria appear to be high in content of Golgi apparatus, can be obtained. These have been studied in various detail (for review and references, see Cook, 1973; Schachter and Rodén, 1973; see also Roseman, 1974). The problem is further complicated by the heterogeneity of membranes within a Golgi stack. Some recent attempts have been made to isolate and characterize the different regions of the Golgi apparatus both by biochemical and cytochemical approaches (Ehrenreich et al., 1973; Bergeron et al., 1973; Farquhar et al., 1974). These techniques may well provide a means for locating transferase activities within different regions of the Golgi stack; however, a note of caution has been sounded with respect to the problem of contamination of isolated membrane fractions, which would be of special importance when trying to work at the "suborganelle" level (Castle et al., 1975).

It would be of particular interest to be able to localize the transferases for galactose, fucose, and sialic acid. These enzymes are clearly involved in final or near-final stages in the attachment of carbohydrate groups that lend specific information characteristics probably both to the contents of the Golgi cisternae and to the membranes. Once at the surface of the cell, these carbohydrate groups may have a profound effect on the behavior of cells (for references, see Cook and Stoddart, 1973). Whereas it is not yet possible to determine whether these enzymes are asymmetric in their distribution within the Golgi apparatus, the evidence presented here as to the high degree of specialization within the organelle (see also Leblond and Bennett, 1974) would suggest that they probably are, with a degree of variability that depends on stage of development and activity.

Glycosyltransferases similar to those indicated to be present in or on the membranes of the Golgi apparatus have also been found on the surfaces of some cells where it has been suggested that they may function in aspects of cellular recognition and communication (see Cook and Stoddart, 1973; Roseman, 1970, 1974; Roth, 1973; McLean and Bosmann, 1975). If further investigation verifies this postulate, it would add support

---

in the apparatus and the more mature, highly active secreting cells showed an increased reaction per stack. ×19,000. From Dauwalder et al. (1969).

FIG. 10. Golgi stacks in the alga *Nitella* in a stage of spermatogenesis showing localization of inosine diphosphatase. The reaction product is seen in various cisternae in the stack, but appears to be heavier toward the periphery. N = nucleus. ×26,000.

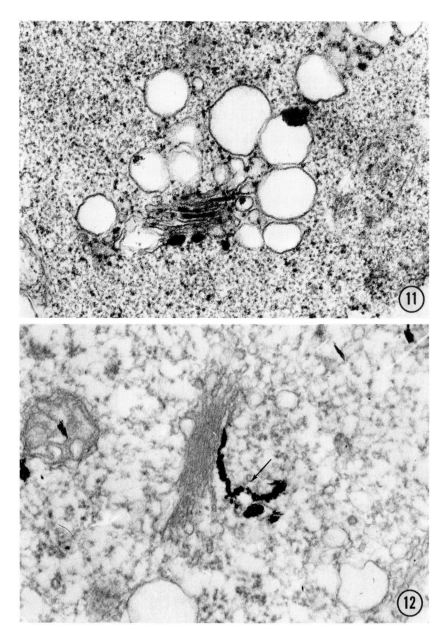

Fig. 11. A Golgi stack from an epidermal cell of the *Zea mays* root tip showing localization of thiamine pyrophosphatase. The reaction product is seen in various cisternae in the stack whereas in other systems investigated it may be discretely localized at the distal face. ×59,500. From Dauwalder *et al.* (1969).

to the concept that the Golgi apparatus gives rise to the plasma membrane and that many of the capacities of the cell surface membrane to act in "messenger" roles for the cell are developed during the differentiation of the cisternae of this organelle.

IV. Synthesis and Attachment of Polysaccharides

The polarity of maturation of the cisternae can also be readily demonstrated by radioautography. It was made clear long ago (for references, see Leblond, 1965; Palade, 1966) that proteins containing labeled amino acids are transferred from the rough endoplasmic reticulum to the more distal cisternae, or to membrane-bounded vesicles derived from them. Despite the attractiveness of the idea of transfer in membrane-bounded vesicles, the mechanism of this transfer is still unknown (for a recent view, see Meldolesi, 1974). It appears to be a quantal transfer (Jamieson and Palade, 1967a,b) and in many instances to be protein to which some carbohydrates have already been attached. The radioautographic pattern following the incorporation of certain sugars, notably glucose (Peterson and Leblond, 1964a,b; Neutra and Leblond, 1966a; Northcote and Pickett-Heaps, 1966; Leffingwell, 1970), galactose (Neutra and Leblond, 1966b; Whur et al., 1969; G. Bennett, 1970; Weinstock and Leblond, 1971; Dauwalder and Whaley, 1974), and fucose (G. Bennett and Leblond, 1970; Haddad et al., 1971; G. Bennett et al., 1974), is quite different. The Golgi apparatus is rapidly labeled without evidence of prior labeling of the endoplasmic reticulum, and often the incorporated label is limited to the region of the organelle toward the distal face or in secretion vesicles being formed at this face. Figure 13 shows the labeling, following glucose incorporation, of the more distal cisternae of the Golgi apparatus and clearly in apparatus-derived vesicles. It also shows considerable transfer to the cell surface. Figure 14 shows an indication of a distal face and/or vesicle labeling with galactose, and Fig. 15 shows a similar pattern following the incorporation of acetate. Although the radioautographic technique does not allow a definitive interpretation, this pattern might indicate the presence of active glycosyltransferases at this site or perhaps the preferential absorption of the sugars directly through the more mature membranes of the Golgi apparatus, where they are attached to assembling glycoproteins or mucopolysaccharides. The functions of some of these compounds at the surface of the cell apparently depend on their sulfation. Both Neutra and Leblond (1966b) and Young

---

FIG. 12. A Golgi stack from the rootcap of *Zea mays* showing localization of acid phosphatase. The reaction product is limited to the distalmost cisterna and/or GERL (arrow). ×55,500.

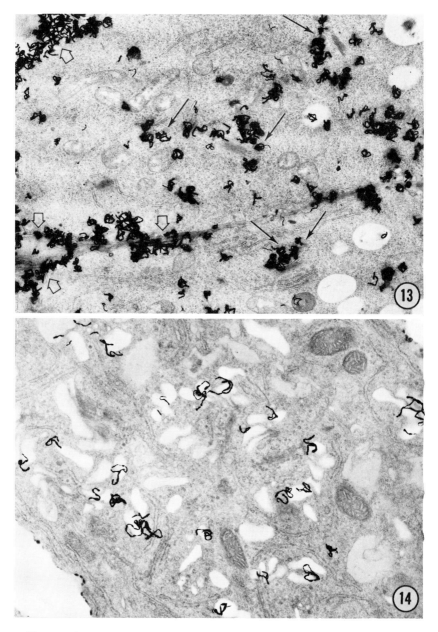

Fɪɢ. 13. An electron microscope radioautograph of a portion of an epidermal cell of *Zea mays* following 30 minutes of incorporation of ³H-labeled glucose. The silver grains are found predominantly over groups of secretory vesicles at the distal face of the Golgi stacks (long arrows). With this time period, labeling of the cell surface is also seen (short arrows). ×10,500. From Dauwalder *et al.* (1969).

(1973) have shown the sulfation to take place in the Golgi apparatus, and Young has demonstrated the presence of the enzymes responsible in the organelle.

The distribution of polysaccharides in the Golgi apparatus can also be demonstrated by a number of different, relatively nonspecific stains (see Rambourg, 1971) (Fig. 16). It is still to be ascertained whether the specific lectins useful as cell surface indicators of carbohydrate groups can differentiate among the polysaccharides synthesized in the Golgi apparatus, but the prognosis appears hopeful (see Etzler and Branstrator, 1974; Wood et al., 1974).

A quite different view of the polarity of the Golgi apparatus and additional aspects of the differentiation of the Golgi cisternae can be made clear by modifications of certain impregnation techniques. For example, with osmium and osmium–zinc iodide, some secretory products are usually unstained, there is generally staining of the proximal face of the organelle (Fig. 17), and in some cases staining of both faces with unstained cisternae in the middle (Fig. 18) (see Friend and Murray, 1965; Novikoff et al., 1971; Dauwalder and Whaley, 1973; Rambourg et al., 1973). The interpretation of these patterns is not yet clear; however, the presence of distinct differences within the stack seems unquestionable.

Perhaps the best case that the functioning of the Golgi apparatus represents a specialized part of the genetically controlled operation of the cell can be made for the assembly of certain glycoproteins. Dische (1966) has called attention to the fact that glycoproteins and also glycolipids can come to bear enhanced molecular information, and Roseman (1974) has called attention to the control of their formation, molecular characteristics, and some of their functions. It appears that whether carbohydrate is introduced into the Golgi apparatus as part of a glycoprotein or glycolipid molecule, or is absorbed directly, its incorporation into developing macromolecules is a characteristic of the more distal face cisternae or associated vesicles, at least when the Golgi apparatus is in the differentiated, or secreting, form.

V. The Golgi Apparatus and the Cell Surface

Increasing evidence indicates that the plasma membrane is a highly patterned mosaic structure, the outer surface of which may be "studded" with numerous enzymes, recognition groups, receptor sites, etc. Concern

---

FIG. 14. An electron microscope radioautograph of a portion of an outer rootcap cell of Zea mays following 30 minutes of incorporation of ³H-labeled galactose. The silver grains are localized over the forming secretory vesicles. With this time period, labeling of regions of the cell surface toward the periphery of the rootcap is also seen (Dauwalder and Whaley, 1974). ×13,000.

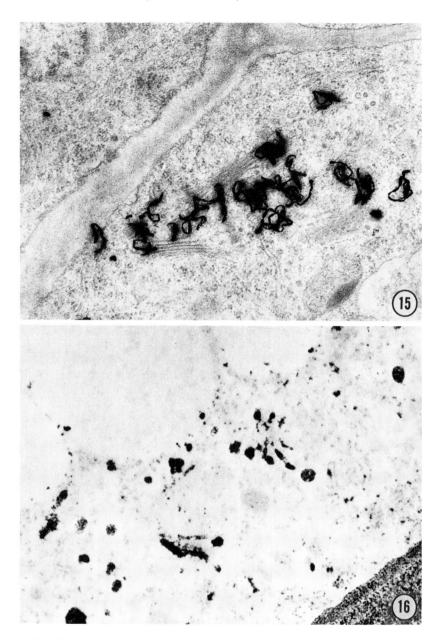

Fig. 15. An electron microscope radioautograph of a portion of an epidermal cell of *Zea mays* following 15 minutes of incorporation of ³H-labeled acetate. In this system the incorporated acetate appeared to go primarily into carbohydrate synthesis: the pattern of incorporation was similar to that with glucose, the secreted wall materials were highly labeled, and neither the labeling of the Golgi apparatus

here is directed primarily toward the carbohydrate moieties of surface materials, since accumulating evidence points to their particular importance in conferring various specificity characteristics to cell surfaces and there is a preponderance of evidence linking the synthesis and transport of such materials to the Golgi apparatus [see, however, Hausman and Moscona (1975) for an example of specificity in the protein moiety].

The involvement of the Golgi apparatus in the incorporation of certain hexoses and the synthesis of polysaccharides, quite possibly in combination with protein or lipid moieties, has been suspected for some time (for references, see Whaley, 1975). This subject has been treated in some detail by Cook and Stoddart (1973), who referred particularly to the work of Neutra and Leblond (1966a,b) and Whur et al. (1969) and concluded that as a stage in the synthesis of glycoproteins, this has been unequivocally demonstrated. Cook and Stoddart look upon the frequent demonstration of glycosyltransferases in the Golgi apparatus as representing an ultimate stage in primary genetic control. The same must be true of other enzymatic proteins in or on the differentiated Golgi apparatus membranes. Cook and Stoddart interpret the formation of the conjugated compounds, including antigenic materials, which come to have importance on the cell surface as representing a secondary stage in the expression of genetic control. This separation of primary and secondary stages is in a way unfortunate, though it is in accord with current genetic thinking. At any rate it implies that the order of synthesis and assembly of products that may provide special characteristics for the cellular surface occurs in a sequence that includes the Golgi apparatus, where particular sugar sequences are added (for references, see Hughes, 1973) and changes in the proteins may take place. Winzler (1970) established that the glycoproteins on the surface of erythrocytes contained, among other polysaccharides, those known from general evidence to include the ones added to the protein groups in the Golgi apparatus. He also recognized that these surface characteristics determine various aspects of cell recognition, cellular compatibility, agglutination, and a whole range of considerations that assure the regularity of cellular development or the breakdown of this regularity in certain dysfunctions. The presence of these sugars has now also been shown to be a characteristic of the surface

---

vesicles nor of the secreted materials was removed by lipid extraction procedures that did remove the minor amount of radioactivity found over lipid droplets. The grains are again localized at the distal face of the Golgi stack and/or over the secretory vesicles. ×27,500.

FIG. 16. Golgi stacks in an outer rootcap cell of Zea mays showing staining of the secretory materials by a periodic acid, silver Schiff's method for the demonstration of polysaccharides. ×17,000. From Dauwalder et al. (1969).

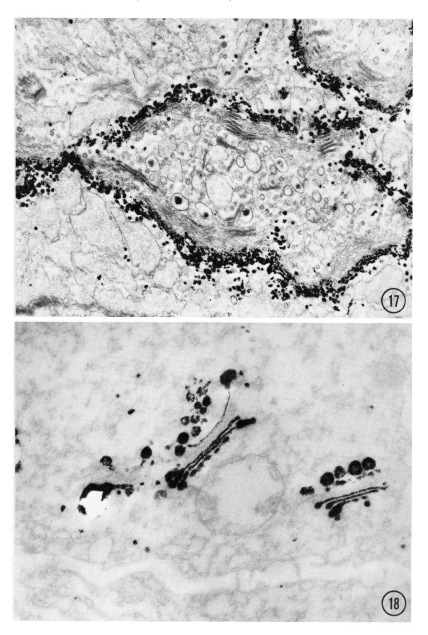

Fɪɢ. 17. A portion of the Golgi apparatus from the multifid gland of *Helix aspersa* after osmium impregnation. As compared with Fig. 2 it can be seen that the cisternae impregnated are limited to the proximal face. ×18,000.

Fɪɢ. 18. Golgi stacks from a cell from the cortex of the *Zea mays* root tip after of many other types of cells, including specifically immunologically competent ones (Aminoff, 1970; Hughes, 1973). The implication is that surface factors, including immunologically important groups, are the immediate products of the active, genetically controlled differentiation of the Golgi apparatus. It ought to be emphasized that specific glycolipids are also involved in surface-mediated processes, and it should be noted that Cook and Stoddart (1973) contend that the genetic control of certain blood group antigens might well represent a situation in which more specific knowledge about genetic control of cell surface characteristics might be acquired (see also Steck, 1974).

VI. Comments

It is generally accepted that the components of cellular membranes are synthesized in the endoplasmic reticulum and then, by processes as yet undefined, transferred to the organelles characterized by membrane assembly and growth. However, in making this assumption, most investigators have concerned themselves with proteins or lipids, although there is evidence that in some instances such hexoses as N-acetylglucosamine and mannose are attached to specific amino acids early in the assembly process (see Schachter and Rodén, 1973). Current studies in membrane structure and metabolism (for references, see Siekevitz, 1972; McMurray, 1973) suggest that there is a continuing turnover in membranes, much more rapid in some instances than in others. Actually, it may be possible to distinguish between two functionally quite different types of membranes in the cell. Some of the membranes of such organelles as the mitochondria and the plastids (Racker, 1970) are composed of repetitive units which compartmentalize metabolic processes in a manner that makes for great efficiency. Although distinct regions of the plasma membrane may display similar features (for example, the outer segment of the retinal rod and "gap" junctions), this membrane is generally a much more heterogeneous structure, as also appears to be the case for the endoplasmic reticulum and the Golgi apparatus. The plasma membrane has a great many specific characteristics related in part to the presence of polysaccharide groups in genetically modulated patterns, which participate in cellular recognition and other factors determining cellular compatibility, adhesion, and many other fundamental activities that are part of the basic aspects of cell sociology. In assembly on the proximal face of the Golgi apparatus these membranes resemble the glycoprotein–lipid

osmium–zinc iodide impregnation. Cisternae at both faces show staining with a lack of staining in the mid-region of the stack. In this system the pattern of staining was dependent on the state of differentiation of the cell. ×38,500.

systems that are established for some other intracellular membrane systems. It now seems beyond a doubt that the synthesis of numerous specific polysaccharides and their assembly in fixed patterns is a result of activities in the Golgi apparatus which differentiate these membranes for the production of specific secretory products as well as the lending of critical characteristics to the cell surface. Neither does there seem to be doubt that there is recirculation of components and continuing modification of these membranes as one of the features of cell differentiation and aging.

Cook and Stoddart (1973) as well as other investigators (see Rambourg, 1971; Whaley *et al.*, 1972; Dauwalder *et al.*, 1972; Leblond and Bennett, 1974) have discussed at length the presence of heterosaccharides on the cell surface, and many have stressed their importance in cellular recognition. Moscona (1974b) has added to the work by numerous authors summarizing the effects of surface membranes on various aspects of development. Hughes (1973) has emphasized the extreme specificity of the glycosylation enzymes involved in the assembly of the surface-conjugated groups containing polysaccharides. The evidence presented here and by other investigators all suggests a maturation of Golgi apparatus cisternae involving certain of these groups, whether by progressive displacement or some other process, and it is of importance to recognize this maturation, and if possible discover how it comes about. The assembly of surface substances with the full characteristic complex of carbohydrates could well depend upon the transfer of certain enzymatic proteins or coenzymes; the spatial distribution of enzymes, or the interrelations between these agents of the genes and the other membrane components after differentiation in the Golgi apparatus. Deficiencies could result from a breakdown in this differentiation, or errors in assembly or transfer or some other prior process. If in fact such deficiencies (see Roth, 1973) are frequent enough to interfere with the efficient destruction of potentially malignant cells by immunological processes, then modification of the function of the Golgi apparatus could be a factor in the development of neoplasias as well as many other dysfunctions. Evidence (see Davidsohn and Ni, 1970; Hakomori *et al.*, 1972; Marx, 1974) suggests that such modifications are likely due to failure of the organelle to produce some essential heterosaccharides, somewhat as failure of the organelle to process specific lysosomal enzymes is reponsible for certain storage diseases (see de Duve, 1969; Hers and Van Hoof, 1973). Roth (1973) has presented a review setting up a model which assumes that immunologically deficient and otherwise developmentally incompetent cells may lack the normal complement of surface polysaccharides, and thus fail to respond in normal developmental patterns. Burger and his group (see

Burger, 1971a,b, 1974) have assembled evidence showing that conditions resulting in such deficiencies on the cell surface somehow interfere with the normal influence of contact inhibition, and the result may be continuing cell division. Fox *et al.* (1971) and Burger (1974) have shown the surfaces of normal cells in division to have characteristics similar to the surfaces of transformed cells. If these surface characteristics are in part determined by the Golgi apparatus, then modification of the Golgi apparatus, sometimes visible in abnormal situations, may include a failure of the development of the enzymatic proteins. The communication between the surface and the nucleus basic to the interpretation of Burger and Fox may in part be mediated by molecular exchanges at the membrane or even endocytosis. Through its functioning in relation to the lysosomal system, the Golgi apparatus also plays a part in metabolic processes following the return of surface-associated materials to the cytoplasm (see Dingle, 1969; Dauwalder *et al.*, 1972).

Whether the concern is with normal development or dysfunctions, there is increasing recognition that events are largely controlled by dynamic membranes. The nature of these membranes is genetically conditioned, and a large part of the initial development of their unique components, even of surface membranes, is intracellular. This proposition furnishes the grounds for more logical explanations of many morphogenetic considerations. The function of the Golgi apparatus, both in assembling and extending membranes and in polysaccharide synthesis, makes it a late stage in the expression of genetic control, though modifications at the surface clearly take place. The pattern of differentiation of the Golgi apparatus indicates that in most cases assembly of its membranes comes first. Then the membranes are characterized to mediate the functions that implement the characteristics of the cell surfaces as well as of the secretory products. Interpretation of the functioning of the Golgi apparatus should be broadened to include the possible transfer of genetically characterized, information-packed membrane subject to replacement during development and to modification in dysfunctions.

ACKNOWLEDGMENT

This investigation was supported by a grant from the Faith Foundation.

REFERENCES

Aminoff, D., Ed. (1970). "Blood and Tissue Antigens." Academic Press, New York.
Benes, F., Higgins, J. A., and Barrnett, R. J. (1973). *J. Cell Biol.* **57**, 613–629.
Bennett, D., Boyse, E. A., and Old, L. J. (1972). *In* "Cell Interactions" (L. G. Silvestri, ed.), pp. 247–263. North-Holland Publ., Amsterdam.
Bennett, G. (1970). *J. Cell Biol.* **45**, 668–673.
Bennett, G, and Leblond, C. P. (1970). *J. Cell Biol.* **46**, 409–416.
Bennett, G., Leblond, C. P., and Haddad, A. (1974). *J. Cell Biol.* **60**, 258–284.

Bergeron, J. J. M., Ehrenreich, J. H., Siekevitz, P., and Palade, G. E. (1973). *J. Cell Biol.* **59**, 73–88.

Boyse, E. A. (1973). *In* "Current Research in Oncology 1972" (C. B. Anfinsen, M. Potter, and A. N. Schechter, eds.), pp. 57–94. Academic Press, New York.

Bretscher, M. S. (1974). *In* "The Cell Surface in Development" (A. A. Moscona, ed.), pp. 17–27. Wiley, New York.

Brown, R. M., Jr. (1969). *J. Cell Biol.* **41**, 109–123.

Burger, M. M. (1971a). *Biomembranes* **2**, 247–270.

Burger, M. M. (1971b). *Curr. Top. Cell Regul.* **3**, 135–193.

Burger, M. M. (1974). *In* "Macromolecules Regulating Growth and Development" (E. D. Hay, T. J. King, and J. Papaconstantinou, eds.), pp. 3–24. Academic Press, New York.

Castle, J. D., Jamieson, J. D., and Palade, G. E. (1975). *J. Cell Biol.* **64**, 182–210.

Cook, G. M. W. (1970). *In* "Molecular Biology" (A. Haidemendkis, ed.), pp. 179–207. Gordon & Breach, New York.

Cook, G. M. W. (1973). *In* "Lysosomes in Biology and Pathology" (J. T. Dingle, ed.), Vol. 3, pp. 237–277. North-Holland Publ., Amsterdam.

Cook, G. M. W., and Stoddart, R. W. (1973). "Surface Carbohydrates of the Eukaryotic Cell." Academic Press, New York.

Dales, S. (1971). *In* "Cell Membranes. Biological and Pathological Aspects" (G. W. Richter and D. G. Scarpelli, eds.), pp. 136–144. Williams & Wilkins, Baltimore, Maryland.

Dauwalder, M., and Whaley, W. G. (1973). *J. Ultrastruct. Res.* **45**, 279–296.

Dauwalder, M., and Whaley, W. G. (1974). *J. Cell Sci.* **14**, 11–27.

Dauwalder, M., Whaley, W. G., and Kephart, J. E. (1969). *J. Cell Sci.* **4**, 455–497.

Dauwalder, M., Whaley, W. G., and Kephart, J. E. (1972). *Sub-Cell. Biochem.* **1**, 225–276.

Davidsohn, I., and Ni, L. Y. (1970). *Acta Cytol.* **14**, 276–282.

de Duve, C. (1969). *In* "Lysosomes in Biology and Pathology" (J. T. Dingle and H. B. Fell, eds.), Vol. 1, pp. 3–40. North-Holland Publ., Amsterdam.

Della Torre, G. (1974). *J. Ultrastruct. Res.* **48**, 388–395.

Dingle, J. T. (1969). *In* "Lysosomes in Biology and Pathology" (J. T. Dingle and H. B. Fell, eds.), Vol. 2, pp. 421–436. North-Holland Publ., Amsterdam.

Dische, Z. (1966). *In* "Protides of the Biological Fluids" (H. Peeters, ed.), pp. 1–20. Elsevier, Amsterdam.

Ehrenreich, J. H., Bergeron, J. J. M., Siekevitz, P., and Palade, G. E. (1973). *J. Cell Biol.* **59**, 45–72.

Etzler, M. E., and Branstrator, M. L. (1974). *J. Cell Biol.* **62**, 329–343.

Farquhar, M. G., Bergeron, J. J. M., and Palade, G. E. (1974). *J. Cell Biol.* **60**, 8–25.

Fox, T. O., Sheppard, J. R., and Burger, M. M. (1971). *Proc. Nat. Acad. Sci. US* **68**, 244–247.

Friend, D. S., and Murray, M. J. (1965). *Amer. J. Anat.* **117**, 135–149.

Grove, S. N., Bracker, C. E., and Morré, D. J. (1968). *Science* **161**, 171–173.

Haddad, A., Smith, M. D., Herscovics, A., Nadler, N. J., and Leblond, C. P. (1971). *J. Cell Biol.* **49**, 856–882.

Hakomori, S., Kijimoto, S., and Siddiqui, B. (1972). *In* "Membrane Research" (F. C. Fox, ed.), pp. 243–277. Academic Press, New York.

Hall, W. T., and Witkus, E. R. (1964). *Exp. Cell Res.* **36**, 494–501.

Hausman, R. E., and Moscona, A. A. (1975). *Proc. Nat. Acad. Sci. U.S.* **72**, 916–920.

Helminen, H. J., and Ericsson, J. L. E. (1968). *J. Ultrastruct. Res.* **25**, 193–213.
Hers, H. G., and Van Hoof, F., Eds. (1973). "Lysosomes and Storage Diseases." Academic Press, New York.
Hicks, R. M. (1966). *J. Cell Biol.* **30**, 623–643.
Hicks, R. M., Ketterer, B., and Warren, R. C. (1974). *Phil. Trans. Roy. Soc., London, Ser B* **268**, 23–38.
Holtzman, E., Novikoff, A. B., and Villaverde, H. (1967). *J. Cell Biol.* **33**, 419–435.
Hughes, R. C. (1973). *Progr. Biophys. Mol. Biol.* **26**, 191–268.
Ito, S. (1974). *Phil. Trans. Roy. Soc., London, Ser B* **268**, 55–66.
Jamieson, J. D., and Palade, G. E. (1967a). *J. Cell Biol.* **34**, 577–596.
Jamieson, J. D., and Palade, G. E. (1967b). *J. Cell Biol.* **34**, 597–615.
Jamieson, J. D., and Palade, G. E. (1971). *J. Cell Biol.* **50**, 135–158.
Kessel, R. G. (1971). *J. Ultrastruct. Res.* **34**, 260–275.
Kraemer, P. M. (1971). *Biomembranes* **1**, 67–190.
Landis. S. C. (1973). *J. Cell Biol.* **57**, 782–797.
Leblond, C. P. (1965). *In* "The Use of Radioautography in Investigating Protein Synthesis" (C. P. Leblond, and K. B. Warren, eds.), pp. 321–329. Academic Press, New York.
Leblond, C. P., and Bennett, G. (1974). *In* "The Cell Surface in Development" (A. A. Moscona, ed.), pp. 29–49. Wiley, New York.
Leffingwell, T. P. (1970). Ph D. dissertation, The University of Texas, Austin.
Levine, A. M., Higgins, J. A., and Barrnett, R. J. (1972). *J. Cell Sci.* **11**, 855–873.
McLean, R. J., and Bosmann, H. B. (1975). *Proc. Nat. Acad. Sci. U.S.* **72**, 310–313.
McMurray, W. C. (1973). *In* "Form and Function of Phospholipids" (G. B. Ansell, J. N. Hawthorne, and R. M. C. Dawson, eds.), pp. 205–251. Elsevier, Amsterdam.
Marx, J. L. (1974). *Science* **183**, 1279–1282.
Meldolesi, J. (1974). *Phil. Trans. Roy. Soc., London, Ser B* **268**, 39–53.
Meldolesi, J., Jamieson, J. D., and Palade, G. E. (1971a). *J. Cell Biol.* **49**, 109–129.
Meldolesi, J., Jamieson, J. D., and Palade, G. E. (1971b)). *J. Cell Biol.* **49**, 130–149.
Meldolesi, J., Jamieson, J. D. and Palade, G. E. (1971c). *J. Cell Biol.* **49**, 150–158.
Mollenhauer, H. H., and Morré, D. J. (1966). *Annu. Rev. Plant. Physiol.* **17**, 27–46.
Morré, D. J., Mollenhauer, H. H., and Bracker. C. E. (1971). *In* "Origin and Continuity of Cell Organelles" (J. Reinert and H. Ursprung, eds.), pp. 82–126. Springer-Verlag, Berlin and New York.
Moscona, A. A., Ed. (1974a). "The Cell Surface in Development." Wiley, New York.
Moscona, A. A. (1974b). *In* "The Cell Surface in Development" (A. A. Moscona, ed.), pp. 67–99. Wiley, New York.
Neutra, M., and Leblond, C. P. (1966a). *J. Cell Biol.* **30**, 119–136.
Neutra, M., and Leblond, C. P. (1966b). *J. Cell Biol.* **30**, 137–150.
Northcote, D. H. (1971a). *Symp. Soc. Exp. Biol.* **25**, 51–69.
Northcote, D. H. (1971b). *Endeavour* **30** (109), 26–33.
Northcote, D. H. (1973). *In* "Cell Biology in Medicine" (E. E. Bittar, ed.), 197–214. Wiley, New York.
Northcote, D. H., and Pickett-Heaps, J. D. (1966). *Biochem. J.* **98**, 159–167.
Novikoff, A. B. (1965). *In* "Intracellular Membraneous Structure" (S. Seno, and E. V. Cowdry, eds.), pp. 277–290. Chugoku Press, Okayama, Japan.
Novikoff, P. M., Novikoff, A. B., Quintana, N., and Hauw, J.-J. (1971). *J. Cell Biol.* **50**, 859–886.
Oseroff, A. R., Robbins, P. W., and Burger, M. M. (1973). *Annu. Rev. Biochem.* **42**, 647–682.

186   W. G. WHALEY, M. DAUWALDER, AND T. P. LEFFINGWELL

Ovtracht, L., and Thiéry, J.-P. (1972). *J. Microsc. (Paris)* **15**, 135–170.
Palade, G. E. (1966). *J. Amer. Med. Ass.* **198**, 815–825.
Peterson, M., and Leblond, C. P. (1964a). *J. Cell Biol.* **21**, 143–148.
Peterson, M., and Leblond, C. P. (1964b). *Exp. Cell Res.* **34**, 420–423.
Platzer, A. C., and Gluecksohn-Waelsch, S. (1972). *Develop. Biol.* **28**, 242–252.
Racker, E. (1970). *In* "Membranes of Mitochondria and Chloroplasts" (E. Racker, ed.), pp. 127–171. Van Nostrand-Reinhold, Princeton, New Jersey.
Rambourg, A. (1971). *Int. Rev. Cytol.* **31**, 57–114.
Rambourg, A., Marraud, A., and Chrétien, M. (1973). *J. Microsc. (Oxford)* **97**, 49–57.
Roseman, S. (1970). *Chem. Phys. Lipids* **5**, 270–297.
Roseman, S. (1974). *In* "The Cell Surface in Development" (A. A. Moscona, ed.), pp. 255–271. Wiley, New York.
Roth, S. (1973). *Quart. Rev. Biol.* **48**, 541–563.
Schachter, H., and Rodén, L. (1973). *In* "Metabolic Conjugation and Metabolic Hydrolysis" (W. H. Fishman, ed.), Vol. 3, pp. 1–149. Academic Press, New York.
Seegmiller, R., Fraser, F. C., and Sheldon, H. (1971). *J. Cell Biol.* **48**, 580–593.
Seegmiller, R., Ferguson, C. C., and Sheldon, H. (1972a). *J. Ultrastruct. Res.* **38**, 288–301.
Seegmiller, R., Overman, D. O., and Runner, M. N. (1972b). *Develop. Biol.* **28**, 555–572.
Siekevitz, P. (1972). *Annu. Rev. Physiol.* **34**, 117–140.
Sjöstrand, F. S. (1968). *In* "The Membranes" (A. J. Dalton, and F. Haguenau, eds.), pp. 151–210. Academic Press, New York.
Steck, T. L. (1974). *J. Cell Biol.* **62**, 1–19.
Weinstock, A. (1970). *J. Histochem. Cytochem.* **18**, 875–886.
Weinstock, A., and Leblond, C. P. (1971). *J. Cell Biol.* **51**, 26–51.
Whaley, W. G. (1966). *In* "Organisation der Zelle. III. Probleme der biologischen Reduplikation" (P. Sitte, ed.) ; pp. 340–371. Springer-Verlag, Berlin and New York.
Whaley, W. G. (1975). "The Golgi Apparatus," Cell Biology Monographs, Vol. 2. Springer-Verlag, Vienna.
Whaley, W. G., Kephart, J. E., and Mollenhauer, H. H. (1964). *In* "Cellular Membranes in Development" (M. Locke, ed.), pp. 135–173. Academic Press, New York.
Whaley, W. G., Dauwalder, M., and Kephart, J. E. (1971). *In* "Origin and Continuity of Cell Organelles" (J. Reinert and H. Ursprung, eds.), pp. 1–45. Springer-Verlag, Berlin and New York.
Whaley, W. G., Dauwalder, M., and Kephart, J. E. (1972). *Science* **175**, 596–599
Whur, P., Herscovics, A., and Leblond, C. P. (1969). *J. Cell Biol.* **43**, 289–311.
Winzler, R. (1970). *Int. Rev. Cytol.* **29**, 77–125.
Wood, J. G., McLaughlin, B. J., and Barber, R. P. (1974). *J. Cell Biol.* **63**, 541–549.
Yamamoto, T. (1963). *J. Cell Biol.* **17**, 413–421.
Young, R. W. (1973). *J. Cell Biol.* **57**, 175–189.

SUBJECT INDEX

A

Accessory tubules, Golgi-derived, 108–114
Acrosome, secretion by Golgi complex, 105
Adhaerens junctions, 1–34
  cell isolation in, 15–20
  desmosome formation and, 11–26
  development of, 7–15
    abnormal, 10
    formation sequence, 9–10
    normal, 8–9
  structure of, 4–7
Adhesiveness, of cell, measurement of, 129–130
Alpha chains, of extracellular matrix collagen, 38–40
Analytical methods, for extracellular matrix composition, 46–58
Anionic polysaccharides
  of extracellular matrix, 43–45
  analysis, 53–55
  biosynthesis, 67–78, 88–95
  localization, 64–66, 74–78
Aquiferous system, of sponge, differentiation of, 155–157
Archaeocytes, of freshwater sponges, 143

B

Basal laminae, of extracellular matrix, 59

C

Cell differentiation, freshwater sponge in
Cell surface coats, of extracellular matrix, 59–60
  studies of, 141–159
Cells
  in adhaerens junctions, 15–31
  isolation, 15–20
  recombination, 20–31
Cellular recognition, by sponges, 123–140
Choanocytes, of freshwater sponges, 142

Chondrogenesis, glycosaminoglycan synthesis during, 88–95
Chondroitin sulfates, during cartilage development, 88–89
Cisternae, Golgi-derived, 108–114
Collagen
  of extracellular matrix, 38–43
  analysis, 47–53
  biosynthesis, 78–85
  localization, 61–64
Connective tissue, of embryo chick, changing matrix synthesis in, 86–97
Cytochalasin B, desmosome formation in presence of, 20

D

Desmosomes, development of, in adhaerens junctions, 11–15
  formation of, in adhaerens junctions, 20
    cell sorting, 26–28
    foreign cell effects, 21–23
    selective, 23–26

E

Electron microscopy, of extracellular matrix, 58–60
Embryo, extracellular matrix of, 35–102
Enzymes, in Golgi apparatus, differentiation, 169–175
Ephydatia fluviatilis, as material for cell recognition studies, 130–131
Extracellular matrix, 35–102
  anionic polysaccharides of, 43–45
    analysis, 53–55
    biosynthesis, 67–78, 88–95
    localization, 64–66, 74–78
  biochemical analyses of, anatomical correlates, 60–66
  as cellular environment, 36–38
  collagen of, 38–43
    analysis, 47–53
    localization, 61–64

187

A   5
B   6
C   7
D   8
E   9
F   0
G   1
H   2
I   3
J   4